MW01088625

FOR THE SOUL

BARBARA DANIELS DENA

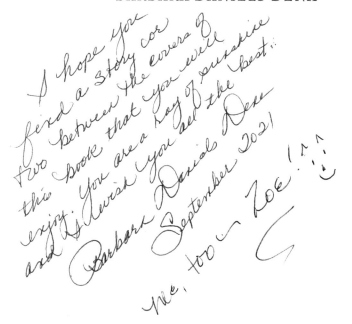

I hope you find a story (or two) between the covers of this book that you will enjoy. You are a ray of sunshine and I wish you all the best.

Barbara Daniels Dena
September 2021

Me, too ~ Zoe!

MAGIC ZOE PUBLISHING

Magic Zoe Publishing

ISBN: 978-0-578-96835-3

For my grandfather, Virgil Neal Daniels, who instilled in me the love of reading at an early age. Many days we sat in a comfortable silence, with him nose deep in a Louis L'Amour old west adventure and me hiding in the shadows of a seedy whodunit. He had a profound influence on my son's reading ability as well. Gramps taught him to read the large print of the gas station logos on state maps years before he began preschool. Later, after my son became a grown man, he told me the well-kept secret that in his early grades, his great-grandfather had paid him a dollar for every library book he finished. Of course, Andy did have to prove it, often from the warm embrace of his great-grandfather's lap. How those two snuck that one by me is their secret. I miss him dearly.

CONTENTS

"The block of granite which was an obstacle in the pathway of the weak becomes a stepping-stone in the pathway of the strong." Thomas Carlyle

In Zen, there is a saying: "The obstacle is the path".

BLACKBIRD

*T*ap, tap, tap. *Again, with that annoying tapping on the windowpane.* TAP, TAP, TAP, repeated a more insistent tapping. *Morse code this early in the morning?*

I knew I was in trouble when I saw the blackbird at my window. "Not again," I moaned as I acted like a rabbit and burrowed farther beneath my blankets and made earmuffs out of my pillow. "The last time you sat on my windowsill, the wicked mother-in-law-to-be visited. Go away."

Tap, tap, tap.

I groaned as I rolled out of my cocoon, intending to shoo away the pesky bird. Icicle shards of cold shot up my legs when my bare feet hit the slate floor.

Tap, tap, tap.

I stood before the window, flapping my hands, knowing full well the beady-eyed guy understood the universal signal to fly away. *Poof, be off with you.* I scrunched my face into my best grimace, the one which scared old ladies, young children, and grumpy salespeople. Not that I used that face often, but it wouldn't hurt to try.

Tap, tap, tap. He continued to stare at me.

I hissed out what could pass for a sigh from a steam engine.

Tap, tap, tap.

Oh, for the love of Peter Rabbit, this was not going well. Two could play this game. I had patience. I would stare him down and wait him out. My eyes were the first to falter, as I had admired Mr. Blackbird's glossy feathers. They were not only black but an iridescent combination of black, blue, and green, with a hint of red on the wings.

Tap, tap, tap.

All right, already. If I opened the window, maybe I could scoot the pesky rascal off the windowsill.

Mr. Blackbird had other ideas and took flight into my castle in the sky before I could try out my scooting technique. He gave two flaps and stuck a ten-point landing on the corner of my scarred wooden desk.

"Make yourself at home," I said sarcastically. *Did birds understand sarcasm?*

His shimmering feathered head bobbed his thanks. He began pecking at the raisins on my flea market treasure. He followed it with a chaser of water from the full, highball glass sitting to the left of the fairy tale story I had been writing before I went to bed.

"I didn't mean it literally." I giggled as I wiggled my toes into my fuzzy, puppy-faced slippers, and cuddled myself into the red threadbare robe that warmed me through my college years. I then eased into my grandmother's antique spindle-back chair to watch him.

I wondered why a blackbird's reputation paralleled signs of bad luck. Possibly the color black, which always appeared to be an indicator of a dreadful event? Maybe.

I sat mesmerized as I studied how the guest at my desk enjoyed his treat. Then, as I concentrated on the beauty of his feathers, one plume followed by another began fading from the brilliant black color to shades of gray, beige, and finally to all white.

While I sat in a total state of shock, he spoke. "Blackbirds are tricksters. You see before you a virtual transformation of my ability. Don't believe the false rumors that our black color is a harbinger of bad things to come. We have delivered good omens and offered protective totems throughout the ages. This morning, I observed you are a kind person as shown by your actions in allowing me to dine here. I foretell it, my lady, good fortune will come your way."

Tap, tap, tap. TAP, TAP, TAP sounded the insistent pecking on the flat writing surface, which brought me out of my self-imposed trance. I watched as the shimmering solid white bird launched himself to the open window, stopped at the windowsill, gave me a farewell flap of his wings, and drifted out on the early morning's gentle wind.

After Mr. Blackbird left me to my thoughts, I wobbled back to my bed. *Birds don't talk, birds don't change color. Blackbirds don't bring good news.* I chuckled to myself as a peaceful sleep returned to me.

Tap, tap, tap. My roommate's fingernail code on my door woke me up.

"What?" I growled.

"A registered letter came for you. I'll slip it under the door. It looked important…. from that publishing house where you submitted your book," said the hesitant voice on the other side of the closed door.

I yawned and rubbed the sleep from my eyes as I tried to unfurl myself from the swaddle of blankets, I slept in. The weirdest dream crept through my mind as I hobbled to the door. After I bent to retrieve the letter, I felt an icy breeze, jolted upright, and gaped at the open window where a white feather lay.

November 2018

This was a challenge by an author friend to write a story about a blackbird.

BOX OF KEYS

My box of keys was a walk down memory lane with each key bringing to my mind places of great importance in my life. One memory key I held is to the front door of my grandparent's home. They have long since passed, the home sold, and the outside refurbished by new owners. I often drive by, recall days long past, and fondly remember the family patriarch.

He walked with a regal bearing, sat high in the saddle, and used holistic medicine to cure both animal and human. We considered him the family historian, wise sage, and unwillingly the blunt end of many family jokes. One of the most famous was the time in which he kept a bottle of his favorite alcohol in the freezer. With medicinal purposes in mind, of course, it was better ice cold. He liked to have a tiny nip now and again, and hopefully away from the disapproving eyes of Grandma. This went on for some time until the day she discovered the liquid in the bottle was partially frozen. Not until then had she realized he added water to the bottle each time he favored himself with a little "medicine." Apparently, he hadn't wanted her to know how many nips he needed to feel better but failed to remember the water would freeze.

I held the key in my hand and recalled the well-known respect he established as a local leatherworker for our area horsemen. One day, to my amazement, he handed me a gift of a leather harness. I did not have a horse. He knew that, but I had an over-active little boy who wandered off in a crowd. My grandfather had fashioned a harness for him so he would experience a little "horse training" and control. Apparently, in his mind, my parenting skills needed a bit of training as well.

I wondered, also, if this might have been a tongue-in-cheek gentle reminder of our horse days when it had been his dream for me to become a jockey for his quarter horse. Oh, how he eagerly anticipated the day when I would be lifted up on Festus' back and ride to the finish line with both our manes flying. Alas, on the day of the weigh-in, when he felt the training time had arrived, I had passed the 110-pound designated weight goal. I was short enough, but a few pounds over his ideal girl-jockey weight. His dream went up in smoke, dooming me to cleaning stalls.

Unknown to Gramps, worry-free days gave me the

luxury of watching the horses versus sitting atop one as I did not care for riding horses. I imagined racing one of those beasts at breakneck speed around a track, not only holding on for dear life but guiding the horse to a win was a fool's game. All right, I admitted wearing those gorgeous, flowing silks made a cool fashion statement but being on the ground had its advantages also, like Wrangler butt cowboys.

When it came to boys, Gramps loved to give his advice on my appearance for the evening dates, and he also gave unasked for recommendations on how I should conduct myself. If the skirt appeared too mini or hair too teased, he would give me a twirling motion with his index finger. If he added the dreaded upward flip of that twirling finger, I must return to my room and change whatever had displeased him. I would go stomping back to my upstairs bedroom to repair my look into an outfit more suitable for his inspection.

"DON'T SLOUCH," HE WOULD SAY, "THROW BACK YOUR shoulders and be proud you are a woman." Thank goodness these conversations took place before the young man arrived.

The key I held also let me in the door at curfew. Fiddling with setting the clocks backward, enabling me to stay out an hour longer, did not work. Gramps knew my tricks. He would just wait up for me.

My years were full of these 'key' stories. I lived

with my grandparents during my summers and college years, and those days were always memorable. His advice and wisdom were sound. *Like the time when he would not let me ride in a car with two drunk teenage friends.*

"What's not to like about it?" he would say. This made no difference to him if I had an aversion to riding horses or eating his morel mushrooms. This was his philosophy on life. He and Jean-Luc Picard could have been one and the same.

"Make it so" would easily have been a directive from my grandfather. Anyone who worked with or knew him would have been happy to be his number one. His requests were few, his words were golden, and his heart was true.

I may have held the key to his home, but he always held the key to my heart. I was his granddaughter. I was his number one.

Fall 2017

In 2019, In a drive-by moment, a girlfriend and I saw the new owners of the old family home. Carbon Cliff, Illinois. We stopped to introduce ourselves and asked if they would like the history of the home and the area (all of which my family owned at one time). They declined, much to our surprise. *This gave us pause to wonder why?*

ll Annie could see in the rear-view mirror was the head of her young son, her floppy-eared dog, and the drunken man running after the car at full stretch. She was free. They were running for their lives, but they were free.

LOSING OUT ON THE ADVERTISED JOB WAS A BLOW TO her ego. The truth of the matter was that the interviewer's predictions were right. Annie's emotions were raw, and the healing would take time. She was not mentally prepared to take on the responsibilities of this position.

"I'm sorry, but I can't offer you the job. Your life experiences will catch up with you and will make it difficult for you to cope with the abuse these women have been through," the personnel associate said.

"I have the qualifications," Annie argued. "I am perfectly capable of hearing the details of what the ladies have experienced. Remembering and sharing what I've been told helps in the healing process. I'm not like these other women."

"YOU NEVER TAKE THE CAR AND MY CHILD AWAY AGAIN without my permission, do you hear me? I will always find you and drag you back home."

"*If I had only followed along, my life would have been fine.*"

"You better shape up or I'm not coming home tonight," he would say.

Night after night, she would wait for him to stumble in. She would lie awake thinking, "S*hould I pray for his safe return or no return at all? Maybe an accident will end this family's misery.*"

In the end, he'd stagger in, knocking into furniture, talking to himself, missing the bathroom, and passing out where he fell. Once sleep overtook him, her panic stopped, although she never knew if the sheriff would be ringing the bell to arrest him for an offense he committed while intoxicated.

Blackouts were a way of life. The next day was always full of "What is your problem? Can't I stop to have a beer with the guys?"

"You're not wearing that in public if you're going

out with me," he ordered on occasions too numerous to count. From being the proud, loving husband at the start of their marriage to a brow-beating tyrant who emerged as time wore on,

Living with him was comparable to being held hostage by a demanding overseer when it came to her appearance. He would insist she wasn't to wear any leisure clothes or sandals in public. Heaven forbid that she'd even consider wearing sweat suits or jogging clothes to the grocery store.

Since Annie was a working woman, Mr. Tyrant commanded her to wear full make-up and proper dress when she left home, regardless of the destination.

Don't forget the damn lipstick. After all, what if someone he worked with were to see her? He would be so embarrassed.

Common demands were to make more money, join more organizations, and increase sales calls to enhance her public persona. The more money she could bring to the family coffers, the more money he could spend.

Annie should've realized trouble was brewing on Christmas Eve when she was late to the dinner table. A tradition of grilling on Christmas Eve was a big deal in his family and to be late was akin to sacrilege. When he gathered up the gifts and quite literally threw them at her for not joining dinner on time, this should have been a clue that violence was a distinct possibility in this man's capabilities. *How much more would she take from this fool?*

Later, he pushed her down the concrete steps. Luckily, she was only bruised in places where no one could see, but there was still the humiliation of wetting herself in front of him. She had run then, too.

Each day, she worked hard at performing her daily housework, gardening, and mealtime preparations in hopes there would be no blowups, or worse, a drinking binge. Life was always worse when he drank. The terrible times were when he insisted that she ride in the car with him, either coming or going to an important event.

"Let me drive. I think you might have had a bit too much to drink," Annie said in her most soothing tone. "Pull over and I will drive us on home while you rest."

"Don't tell me what to do. You are always nagging at me about my drinking," he yelled at her. "I will show you just what I think of your idea. I will pull over all right." He slowed to a stop. As he did so, he reached across the console, unbuckled her seat belt, flipped open the door handle, and pushed at her body twice. With arms reaching to grasp the solid door and finding nothing but the humid night air, she began falling, landing on asphalt. She rolled off the pavement into the grass. She could hear screeching tires and doors slamming as she steadied herself.

A good Samaritan picked her up and whisked her to the local hospital, where she was x-rayed and treated for bruised ribs and abrasions. Luckily, there were no broken bones…. this time. She was interviewed by a female officer who wanted her to press charges. Annie was too afraid to do so. They had a lengthy conversation; the officer did not insist that she press charges, although she offered her card in case of another emergency.

The abuse continued. Every time she went to the market, she passed by the police station.

"Karma," she said. "One day."

She still hadn't pressed charges. The incidents mounted. The bruises and excuses no longer made sense to anyone. Her circle of friends shrank as his controlling nature made it difficult to visit and enjoy Annie's hospitality in her home. The invitations and comforting visits soon stopped on both sides of the friendships.

After one long unusually hot summer afternoon, the drinking was heavier than usual. Annie knew she was in for something awful. She could feel it in the air. His temper mounted as the number count of each empty bottle rose.

She saw it before she felt it. The cold steel of the knife slashing through the air. Not that she recalled much after that point, but the pictures they showed her told a good portion of the story. The bruised face and body coupled with the stitches in her side from the knife wound told more of a story than would ever have left her lips.

Her family was bereft once they saw her in this condition, as each arrived one by one at her bedside.

Life was fine for a few days. He was a perfect gentleman, trying to renew the failing relationship after the incident.

"He is probably doesn't remember a thing, only seeing what the pictures showed," she said. "Blackouts never helped him restore his memory before; they certainly will not help him now."

About the time they sat down to dinner, the doorbell rang. She dutifully answered it, and without saying a word, led their dinner company back to the dining room.

"Sir, I have a warrant for your arrest," said the female officer who had befriended Annie in the hospital. "Please stand and put your hands behind your back."

"There must be some mistake," he said through gritted teeth while giving Annie a menacing look.

"No sir, there is no mistake, we have enough reports on your abusive behavior against your wife to put you away for a very long time. Plus, there is the fact that you may have been involved in an illegal drug enterprise. That is yet to be determined. Meanwhile, you may rest in our cozy jail." She then read him his Miranda rights.

Annie smiled for the first time in her recent memory as she recalled her shopping trips. Under the guise of going shopping, she stopped at the police station each time she'd been abused and filled out a report. She asked them to be held until she wanted an arrest warrant to be served.

Karma finally had her day.

This story is a compilation of incidents of abuse which were described to me by ladies who had been there.

"*T*here ain't nothing to it but to do it," quipped Floyd Pepper, bass player for Dr. Teeth and the Mayhem Band in the audition scene of *The Muppet Movie.* My daughter played this movie continuously, and the family could nearly quote it line for line. So, this quote became one I have repeated often in my life.

I used what I thought to be sage wisdom on the occasion when I decided raising Angora rabbits for their wool would be a great money-making idea. That I was a city girl and had never cared for any farm-type animal was immaterial. We had family dogs, but that didn't make a difference. An animal is an animal. So how hard would it be to 'grow' rabbits?

I originally saw Angora rabbits at the county fair. They were fluffy and adorably cute, with the cotton candy tufts of hair on their ears and faces. I spoke to the teenage 4-H handler and gained as much information as possible from her and began a wool-gathering mission of my own. In the '80s wool from a groomed Angora rabbit would sell for sixteen to twenty dollars an ounce. As a reference, a stuffed three-pound Crisco can hold three ounces.

"Now how hard could this be?" I asked myself.

I located a local breeder. She asked, "Do you want a German, French, or English?"

Did they understand different languages? I chose English to be on the safe side.

"And what color?" *Another question.* She raised white, chocolate, black, or champagne. I picked out a white one to start. Later there would be one of each color.

How many more questions?

"For show or for a pet?"

Um. "For spinning wool." *That should do it.*

The breeder showed me her free-range pen. She used hutches only for showtime to keep the rabbits looking good. Otherwise, the bunnies ran free to roam about in their pen. Ladies separate from gents, naturally.

Luckily, I had set up one similar to this. The rabbit's home would be a fenced-in area attached to our garage with a bunny-door cut into the back wall of the garage that opened into an indoor shelter. For added comfort, lovely grapevines surrounded the chain-link enclosure for shade. I had thought of everything.

Next, I was off to buy rabbit pellets and alfalfa. It

wasn't much later when I wished I had asked a few more questions. I had many lessons to learn.

First lesson: We owned three hunting dogs.

One sunny afternoon, I looked out the patio window. Streaking across the back yard scurried one scared rabbit, two setters, and one retriever, all nose to tail, in perfect military precision. Add a screaming, arm-waving mom, and we all ran out of control. It took the rest of the family to help round up our wayward pets. The guilty child confessed he left the bunny pen gate open. Luckily, we only owned one rabbit. A lock on the gate immediately became a priority.

Second lesson: Rabbits burrow.

Right under the garage, they happily burrowed into their own cozy warren. Now, at this time, we owned more rabbits (all females), and wouldn't you know it, down came a rain. Not only a bit of rain but a real gully washer. I insisted my husband retrieve the furballs from under the garage. Drowning would not be an option for the bunnies. I had no worries for the hubby. He would be fine. *I hoped.* The pen reinforcement worked from that day forward, and there was no more nocturnal burrowing under the garage, rain, or shine.

Third lesson: Rabbits may die of shock after being bred for the first time.

Unfortunately, one of ours did. That ended the desire to add to the bunny community. *Well, then how did they have so many baby bunnies? Something seemed amiss in the world of the birds and the bees.*

Fourth lesson: Angoras are extremely sociable animals and loved to be held and groomed.

Groomed? Their wool became matted, if not cared for. All my plans would be lost if not combed regularly. Regularly as in daily, I came to find out. They fluffed out as big as a bushel basket once combed.

Fifth lesson: I could not tug their coat off their warm mini bodies to gather the precious wool. The bunnies were not happy if I tried. *A wiggly, hopping, irritated rabbit is no fun.* The furry friends molted about every ten weeks, and it was then I would gather the wool. Wool was always plucked, never shorn, as the hair follicles kept the non-shedding ability in the clothing made from Angora wool. Shorn wool sheds.

My plans for adding to my bank account looked dim. "Nothing to it but to do it . . ."

Hmm. I rethought this money-making venture, as it was requiring way too much work for a busy mom.

Fast forward.

I eventually found homes for all the bun-buns, except for one.
Special event days at the local zoo found me sitting behind my spinning wheel with a molting rabbit in my lap. She was happy to be the center of attention as I spun her wool right from her

back. I did not fatten my bank account but instead, I had many opportunities on "artist days" at the zoo and grade school to entertain and educate with that one last furry friend. Now, that was well worth teaching myself to 'grow' rabbits.

Fall 1983

CHAPERONE TO THE MARINES

$\mathcal{N}$othing ever surprised me when my boss asked me for a favor. It could be anything from watching the office while he went hunting with the rest of the staff or sitting for an evening with his special needs daughter.

I could not imagine what favor Larry wanted to ask of me. Silly me. He had been asked to take on the position of Special Services Manager for our upcoming Special Olympics Games. Ergo, he was putting together his team. He asked me to take on the role of Transportation Director.

This upcoming May would be the Montana State Special Olympics Games, and apparently it would be "really special" this year as the Special Olympics International Committee would be in attendance holding their annual meeting in conjunction with our games. Such exciting news!

I always participated in Special Olympics no matter in which state I happened to be residing. My role, should I choose to accept it, would entail transporting all dignitaries to and from their specific events and chaperoning the same dignitaries as needed.

Oh, yes, he mentioned that not only was one of my transportation duties to shuttle the SOI Committee to their required events, but also, I was to chaperone the United States Marine Corps Wing Band from El Toro, California to every event. This would include entertainment and meals. *The who? THE PRESIDENT'S OWN BAND? Now, who in her right mind would turn that down!* I was happy to accept the position. It would be an adventure.

A flurry of activities unfolded for the next three months. Scheduling, telephone calls, and meal reservations right along with running my florist all filled the days before the games began. The cars or buses rolled out to greet each set of impressively titled persons as they arrived.

Most striking was the Marine Corps Band. They arrived in their own aircraft. From that point forward, they were mine to command so to speak. Amazingly, they listened to me and followed all my instructions to the letter. The band was a mix of female and male members, and each gender had a separate floor at the Montana State University dorms. Respect was given to me at every step of their stay. Even as I entered the male's floor to give them the itinerary, an alert went out "female on the floor" which made me turn around to see what was happening. It was me, who without a thought entered the male soldier's floor! I took a lot of teasing for that move.

Basically, they were on their own to visit the town when we did not have a tour, special event, or meals to attend. They enjoyed their private time by exploring the shops and eateries of the town. Ceremony time was amazing to view.

Montana extended an invitation to the special athletes from Alaska to join our festivities, and it was my privilege to show them Yellowstone National Park that first year. We did this while the Marines were on their break time in town. These athletes were mesmerized by the elk, but thought caribou were nothing special in their own part of the world.

For opening of the official event, it was my task to make sure each dignitary was in-house and ready to speak at the appropriate time. Now, the funny part of this story was that Peter Fonda was missing. He and his whole family were missing. They had attended another scheduled event at the Museum of the Rockies across the street from the MSU Bobcat Arena and had apparently thought he could "drive" over and enter the festivities under his own steam.

Yikes! I had to find him, so the driver shuttled me in the bus over to the museum, the folding doors flew open as we spied Mr. Fonda. I hopped out, ran across the parking lot, yelling my head off "Mr. Fonda, Mr. Fonda, please stop, you must come with me."

I finally caught up to him, and I tugged on his shirt-sleeve as he apparently had not heard me. Out of breath, I repeated my plea that he must ride my bus over to the arena, or he would not be able to find his way in. He chuckled and did agree to go with the crazy, winded, goofball of a lady.

He was the kindest man and so good to the athletes signing his autograph after the ceremony. He sat on my bus during this time, so I could return him to his car after his "meet and greet". I had no idea where the rest of his family was. I am sure one of the volunteers shuffled them along.

Meanwhile, unbeknown to me, I had instructed my volunteers that no one, and I meant no one could park in the area reserved for the families of the athletes. Apparently, that was a contentious point with many able-bodied attendees. The volunteers succeeded in keeping spaces cleared for those who were unable to walk.

The volunteers succeeded almost too well, as the governor of the state drove into this same parking and drop off area. He was a speaker at the event and tried to enter but was stopped.

He was told, "It makes no difference who you are, we have instructions not to let anyone park here or drive through."

The reply of the confused chauffeur was "But, he is

the Governor." The volunteer (who happened to be my husband) bent down, looked in and said, "Yes, you are right, it really is him. You guys better let him go straight through!" It was a long while before I heard the end of that.

The celebration, of course included an introduction of the SOI Committee and the Athletes March from each of the towns in Montana, plus our invitees from Alaska.

The band did not disappoint and gave a rousing interpretation of patriotic songs as well as the "Marine's Hymn" which is also known as ("The Halls of Montezuma"-1867-Jacques Offenbach), and is the official hymn of the United States Marine Corps. What I found interesting about this hymn was the words were not added until many years later by an anonymous author.

The surprise I had in store for the soldiers was the trip to Manhattan, Montana to Sir Scott's Oasis Steakhouse. Anyone visiting the Bozeman area and loves prime rib is missing a great dinner if they do not visit the "Oasis." But diner beware, no matter who you are, you absolutely cannot eat at the Oasis without reservations.

This is a small, hole in the wall, rustic restaurant with a bar attached. I had the entire restaurant reserved for our special dinner. The bar remained open for the locals. The Marines were so pleased with this meal. After eating, we all assembled outside the restaurant and were to tour Big Sky Carvers located down Main Street. This is a famous wood carving business that I asked to visit with the group.

I teased the Drum Major, who is the senior enlisted member of the band, asking him if they would walk in formation down the street which they did, but he said only if I called the cadence. *Oh sure! That didn't happen.*

As they lined up in front of the building where we were to tour, the Major asked me to release the men, telling me I had to bark out the order reaching down into my diaphragm and really belt it out. As I stood eye to eye with one of the soldiers, (never an eye blink from this young man) I had a fit of the giggles, and what I belted out was more like a squeak. *Oh, well!*

The next morning, the members of the SOI Committee upon hearing about the fun times I had with the Marines were not to be outdone or taken for granted. They sang "Take Me Out to the Ballgame" to me as a gentleman from the San Diego Padres was on board, and they felt that to be a fitting song.

I saw the band off at the airport at the end of the week and received a hug from each of the band members.

The second in command was the Master Sergeant whom I had been instructed to call "Top," and the following year, he would become the Drum Major. The next year was a repeat of the first, with a definite request from the group that we return to the Oasis for dinner again. The second year, we stayed after in the bar/lounge, and the members who felt like it were allowed to bring in their instruments. They played and sang for the patrons.

When not doing so, they played pool, relaxed, and visited with the locals. They sang a special song for me as well and topped the night off with the "Marine Hymn" for those in the bar and the staff.

The end of the second-year visit was an extremely special event for me. My husband went to the dormitory to load them onto the bus for me as I had details to attend to from home before I ventured out to the next event. I would meet them at the airport to see the group off. Little did I know what was about to happen.

The dog barked, the door burst open, and my husband hoped I was fully dressed because there was a surprise in the works. The bus pulled into our cul-de-sac and the Marines unloaded and sang the "Marine Hymn" to me in my front yard. Talk about a shock and a tear-jerker. The good-bye hugs took place here, I didn't need to see them off.

Little did I know that this event was a topic of a radio broadcast after the Marines took off, and I was the talk of the Special Olympics and my Kiwanis comrades for quite some time.

The third year came and was a repeat of the first two except for the closing ceremonies where the Bozeman

High School band was to play. Yes, this band certainly made for an unusual evening.

Top and the Marine Corps band members were sitting in the bleachers with me awaiting their performance and within a heartbeat Top was off the floor bleacher and running to the tuba player in the high school band catching him just as he fainted to the floor. One by one, other members of the band began to fall, and other soldiers were running to the rescue.

I ran forward to the high school band instructor and insisted he remove his people from the arena, telling students to prepare to leave as I ran forward to where the instructor stood near the podium. The arena was full, thousands of people were in attendance wondering what was happening.

In total, we removed seventeen youngsters to the outside cool air. Combined with the heat on the arena floor, the wool uniforms, and locked knees; they all had fainted.

Here were the Marines in action. What an exciting evening, I must say.

The Special Olympics Quilts

DURING THE FIRST YEAR OF THE SPECIAL OLYMPICS, I hit upon the idea of a commemorative quilt to be presented the second year. The idea continued through to the third year as well. The following are tales of our quilts.

THE REVERSIBLE QUILT WAS MADE TO COMMEMORATE the Montana State Special Olympics Games held in Bozeman, Montana, May 1997

Blocks for the quilt front were signed by members of the Special Olympics International Committee including Eunice Kennedy Shriver (Founder of Special Olympics), Sargent Shriver (her husband), Timothy Shriver (her son and Executive Director), Bart Conner (Olympic gymnast and sports commentator), Jay Emmett (executive board member and from the San Diego Padres), Ed Marinaro (actor Hill Street Blues), Tracy York (wife of Ed Marinaro, actress), Amber LePrey (Nashville recording artist), Peter Fonda (actor), Montana governor Marc Racicot, as well as other dignitaries on the International Olympic Executive Committee from around the world and from our area.

I have saved the first original block in my portfolio as it was signed incorrectly by Eunice Kennedy Shriver, so a new one had to be made. (The signature was too close to the seam line and would be lost to view once sewn into the whole quilt.)The quilt back was signed by members of the United States Marine Corps Wing Band, El Toro, California after their meal at the "Oasis." Each member was asked to note home state, instrument played, and a message for the Special Olympics athletes. Each fabric symbolized a part of the Games: the Olympics athletes, the Montana Big Sky, stars, fireworks, musical notes, all with an overall patriotic theme.

Any athlete who passed by the quilt was able to sign his/her name if he/she wished to.

The quilt was to be donated to the Special Olympics after the games. Barbara Dena (me) was the Transportation Director for the games enabling me access to many visitors and to request signatures of the guests on my transport buses.

Addendum 1

The quilt was to remain in Bozeman, Montana in a place to remind us of the games, the athletes, and the wonderful event. No one could decide on a place for it to be displayed on a permanent basis and therefore was never given a home in Bozeman. A couple of years later, I brought the quilt out of storage and sent it to Laurie Shadoan who spearheaded and managed the head of our SO committees. She took a position in Kansas City, Missouri as Manager of that area's Special Olympics. I felt she deserved it, and she knew of all details, stories, people, and the fun times everyone had working under her.

Addendum 2

The following year, the same routine was conducted

with the Marines signing the back of the quilt and this same backing fabric was on display at the Olympic Village for families and athletes to sign. This fabric would be the back to the next quilt and would make the rounds to all the civic organizations that participated in the State Games allowing any volunteer to add their signature and message. Anyway, that was the plan.

When the roving fabric arrived at the Bozeman Rotary Club, the gentleman receiving it threw it away as he did not know what to do with it and believed it to be only a thank you from the athletes to the club and of no significance!! No, he didn't bother to ask me any questions, and I didn't bother to ask him what kind of goofball he was.

Addendum 3

Once again, that same year, the project began, now since we had lost the backing to the quilt, a new idea had to be devised. With the help of other members of the Management Team for the State Games, pictures were located of the previous year's games. They were transferred onto muslin and made into a quilt top, and signatures were sought again from all volunteers of Management Teams, athletes, and the members of Amber LePrey's band.

This quilt, I felt, would be auctioned off at the dinner, but instead a decision was made by the Executive Management Team to give it to Amber LePrey, the

Nashville recording artist who had given of her time so selflessly for three years to help entertain at the games.

She also had a special needs child. A surprise handprint was added to the back of the quilt. This was the handprint I had traced the year before of Amber's little girl. The quilt was presented to the singer at closing ceremonies. I was asked to present it to her but declined as I would be on an airplane flying to Illinois to visit my children at the time of the closing event. The Marines had lifted off earlier that morning before final ceremonies.

I was not available for the public presentation at the morning of the final event, but I understood that it was quite dramatic. A picture of our good friend Larry Wilcox and head of our Management Team showing the signing and presentation was later given to me. Many more people were able to sign the quilt after the festivity. There is also a video of the presentation, but I have never seen it.

Larry Wilcox, a good friend, and my broker when I worked in real estate was the reason I was involved with Special Olympics. He was head of Special Services. I held the title of Transportation Director in this division and under his direction for three years. *What, me needing direction?*

As the bus driver said to me "I gave you the microphone in case they couldn't hear you in the back of the bus, not so you could entertain our guests." *That about sums it up my involvement.*

As a final note to this story, I later received a lovely note from Tim Shriver thanking me for the fun time his group had on my bus. I still have that letter plus the original quilt block signed by his mother, Eunice Kennedy Shriver.

CHICAGO TRAIN

oday, I sat on a pebbly, rough, concrete bench waiting for the Metro train to take me from a suburb of Chicago into Chi town itself. The bench had warmed from the morning sun making the wait comfortable. I had been on my feet all day, and a mixed feeling of tiredness and wellbeing overtook me. The cracked sidewalk lay beneath my feet. Sprouts of green grass forced themselves upward to grab the same rays of sunshine that heated the concrete bench. I watched as trails of ants scurried to and fro at a break-neck speed. *Do ants suffer from road rage?*

I relaxed and thought about the unusual characters I encountered who occupied the sidewalks of Chicago. Of course, there were always the no-nonsense business people who were rude and in a continual hurry. Few took the time for a friendly smile let alone an "excuse me" as they barrel raced around each side of me.

Waiting on the curb for a stoplight to turn green turned into an adventure. People jostled forward when they darn well pleased, walking "Chicago style" totally ignoring light signals.

The homeless saw no problem in approaching pedestrians for a hand-out, shaking a cup of change at us for a donation. Other times straight out asking for money satisfied the task. An offer of food was taken as an insult, as any fool could see, the money was the main goal. A whiff of one hustler left me with an understanding as to where most of the coins in his plastic cup went.

As I sat warming myself on the stone bench, a young man sat down next to me. I imagined him to be in his early twenties, nicely muscled. He had his scalp shaved on both sides of his head with the remainder of his dishwater blond hair spiked straight up. On him, this all looked natural. Maybe it was the sparkling blue eyes or his mischievous smile, but it all blended into a pleasing combination.

His manners were beyond comparison, and he presented himself with a friendly attitude, one of a gentle soul. Yet, as he relaxed, a slump to his shoulders took over and a distant look in those sparkling blue eyes had me wondering if there was a broken man hidden inside of the facade.

We talked about the train schedules and which one we each would be taking into the city. He wanted to hang out back home with his mom and enjoy a home-cooked meal. I would be returning to my son's apartment after a day in a classroom. We eventually worked around to introducing ourselves.

He said, "Hi, my name is Rocky."

I returned with a comment, "Like in *Eye of the Tiger,* Rocky?"

"Ya, my mom loved those movies, sang that song a lot."

"My name is Barbara, Barbara Ann, just like the song," I said.

"The what? The who?" he asked not understanding at all.

"No, not The Who, you know, The Beach Boys, *Barbara Ann,* the Beach Boys song." He sat there, his eyebrows bridging, and eyes glancing about into midair hoping a clue might appear. We both enjoyed a good laugh over the generation gap, especially when I told him to "just Google it."

Finally, he felt comfortable enough to approach me with a question.

"Do you think you could give me fare money, so I can go back into the city?" he asked.

"What?" I said being rather dumbfounded since I obviously misjudged this young man's character. I learned later that this was the norm for the down and out riders at all train stations and had no bearing on his character or the question.

He repeated the question since he obviously thought I had turned deaf in those last few moments. That not being the case and being the kindly old soul that I am, I didn't hesitate in giving him an answer.

"I can do that but are you really going to use it for a fare?" *That's me, right to the point.*

"Yes," he assured me. "I want to go home to see my mom." Whether or not this was true was irrelevant. I liked the young man and was willing to help him out. A gift is a gift and what he did with it really would be none of my business.

We discussed which train he would board, and the fare he required. As I handed over the proper amount, he could no longer contain his curiosity.

"Ma'am will you please tell me why your face is painted like a butterfly?" he asked.

"Oh," I laughed. "I took a class on face painting. It's something I want to do when I retire. That is why I am in Chicago, to learn this art form."

Still laughing, I said, "My kids said since I 'get lost in a shoebox,' I would never be able to find my way out to the suburbs riding the "L" and then the Metro. I told them if you want to do something badly enough you will find a way. I did. I studied and asked questions until I had all the answers on how to find my way here."

He was content with the answer. "It is a very pretty design. Is it hard to remove?" he asked.

"Nope, soap and water."

"Wish I could remove mine, but I will have to live with this forever," he said as he tapped the tattooed teardrop at the corner of his eye.

"That is sad, we do make mistakes in life before we have a chance to really think about what the consequences will be, don't we? I know I sure have made some doozies in my life," I said giving my typical mom advice. "Oh, here is my train. I hope you have a good visit with your mom. I enjoyed talking with you. Take care of yourself."

He waved and I boarded the Metro car. I enjoyed the ride back into the big city. What I found unusual was that no one ventured forward to sit with me. This was fine by me. Those seats were so comfy, I had a double bench all to myself, and no one appeared to need a riding companion. I relaxed until we rolled into the station.

Next, I navigated the station steps, found my way uptown to the "L," and headed to my son's apartment. It was nearing sunset, and the homeless were either setting up in doorways for a night's rest, a private drinking party, or working a last round of pandering. No one approached me for a hand-out, instead looked away, or headed in the opposite direction.

Had I grown a unicorn's horn in the middle of my forehead? This certainly was unusual behavior. I eventually gazed into a large shop window to see what was amiss. I saw nothing wrong. *Then it dawned on me. My face! These folks were spooked by my painted face. That was a real knee slapper.*

This occurred on the subway train also and once again as I passed by the mission where the men waited for their nighttime home to open. This was hilarious to me. I had learned a way to be hassle-free from the panderers in a big city.

After the trek through the mission area, I reached my son's apartment and relayed the day's events. Now **HE** looked at me as if I had indeed grown a unicorn's horn or totally taken leave of any mental ability I may have formerly possessed.

He shook his head "Mom, don't you realize, the young man you talked to had murdered someone in prison, and his tattoo mark indicated this deed to others?" he asked me. The incredulous tone of his voice became evident at how foolish he believed his mother was by talking to this stranger and that my very life could have been in danger.

"Nope, I sure didn't know that," I said in amazement. "And as well as you know your mother, exactly what difference would that have made to me?" *Talking to a murderer? Like that was a big deal. If he only knew about the unusual individuals whom I had spoken to in my life.*

What a day. Ignorance can be bliss. I found it amazing the things one can learn from teaching one's self to ride a train.

Spring 2013

DUST BUNNIES

*M*eg's penance for receiving low marks on her schoolwork this past week kept the daydreamer indoors on this sun-filled Saturday morning. The pony-tailed girl with rich, mahogany-colored hair waggled the pencil between the first two fingers of her left hand as if it were a mini baton. She contemplated the open book on the dining room table. "If only she could figure out a way . . ."

"Don't forget to clean out those dust bunnies from under your bed when you clean your room," Mom said, interrupting her thoughts.

"It's a pod and a cubicle, Mom," Meg said as she watched her whoosh out what she called the front portal and climb into the family's aging imaginary hovercraft.

This is turning into one weird day. I have to stay in all Saturday and study while all my friends are zipping about having fun. Plus, I must sweep up dust bunnies as additional torture for not studying. How demeaning.

"Not to worry, we are all here to save you," said a hoarse voice from the Ficus tree standing at the foot of the stairs leading to the sleeping-pod cubicles as Meg referred to the bedrooms.

"Huh?"

"Over here, kiddo," repeated the voice.

She rose from the swiveling seat, slid over to the floor covered with shedding leaves from the plant, but before she could utter a word . . .

"Your tree is obviously molting," huffed the voice, stopping her in mid-stride. Only this time, it had a warmer, softer tone. In the blink of an eye, a pair of white ears stuck straight up behind the pot of soil holding the tree.

"Exactly who, or what are you?" asked the bewildered, wide-eyed, pony-tailed girl. She knew she should be afraid or at least startled, but her imagination immediately turned on to high alert. *A new tale to write about.*

"All I am trying to do is work on my homework and you are invading not only my private space but quite possibly ruining my mental health."

About this time, the entire floor vibrated. Meg covered her eyes with her hands, hit the floor, and wiggled her way back to hide under the table. When she summoned the courage to peek out between her splayed fingers, all she saw was a streak of black, gray, and white pass by her head to the chair and straight to the tabletop. *This was what caused the massive earthquake-like vibration?*

Meg pushed up from her cowering position on the floor. Placing her open palms on the chair, she peered over the top of the dining room study table. Blinking, she gawked at the sight, gained a bit of courage, and slipped into the chair.

I may have hit my head and am hallucinating. Not able to control her curious nature, her hand reached forward to touch the …

"Don't even try it. Hands to yourself, girlfriend. I will tell you when you may touch me," said the disgusted rabbit, crossing his arms in front of his chest. "With that imagination of yours, surely you can believe your own eyes."

"We are not dust bunnies! 'Demeaning' you say, 'torture?' How rude. We are about to be your best friends, and you will NOT sweep us up."

Not only was she seeing a talking rabbit, but he obviously heard what she said to her mom.

"What's with the pod, cubicle, and hovercraft thing?"

"I like to write stories and change the names of ordinary things. I know perfectly well it is a bedroom, a door, and a car. How boring. It is more interesting when I use my imagination. It is said that left-handed people are more creative, you know." *Oh, boy, now she was talking to the mirage. What will she see next, a faerie?*

"No faeries here, chickee, only rabbits. And that is a

myth about lefties," said the rabbit out loud, obviously confirming the fact that he could read her mind.

A clackety, clacking sound drew their attention as a gray rabbit flew by whacking the table and then hitting a chocolate Oreo cookie with her ever-present hockey stick.

"Goal!" shouted the athletic rabbit, not caring that the cookie shot off the end of the table.

"So, what was the problem at school that you didn't do your homework last week?" asked the white bunny.

"Our school is having the play, *A Tribute to the '80s*, this month, and I tried out for the chorus. The music director told me I had no musical talent, and I couldn't carry a tune in a bucket. I really wanted to be in the musical part of the play. To make matters worse, she accepted every other student in my class except me."

"What kind of monster teacher would say a thing like that?"

"Weren't you listening? The school music teacher, that's who. I was so bummed out and embarrassed, I couldn't concentrate on my homework, not that I even wanted to," said Meg. "Plus, our assignment is to write a creative story for English about the play, and I am NOT about to do that."

Drumming her fingers on the table while staring out into space and recalling that day, she finally looked back at the rabbit. Her curiosity overrode her melancholy, and she asked, "Okay, I will play along. Why are you here?"

"To help you solve your problem." The bossy bunny

ran his paw between his ears and paced the tabletop as he contemplated the set of circumstances that would need to be put into play to right this wrong.

"Circle up, gang, we have a problem to solve. Remember this, my pony-tailed girl, where there is a problem, there is always a solution built-in. We only have to find it."

"My name is Meg, not the pony-tailed girl."

"Well, then since we are on friendly terms now, my name is Sam, and the whiz girl who scored a point with your cookie, calls herself Sticks, for obvious reasons."

As Meg shook her head, she followed the troupe as they hopped, skipped, and jumped back up the stairs to Meg's room. *This ought to be good.*

Here, they hatched out the plan that Sam, the bunny, obviously had in mind. Meg's world was about to change, but she wouldn't be the only shocked one.

As the mastermind laid out his plan, he asked each rabbit to add a suggestion. The completed plan was genius in its hypothesis, but secrecy was the key issue. The most important issue being, could she pull it off?

For the sake of clarity, the group asked Meg to sing for them. There was no doubt she would need vocal training, but that could be developed if she wanted to be a singer. Luckily, they all agreed lip sync would work if needed.

Meg retrieved her MP3 player and downloaded the first song the chorus would be singing. This would give the rabbits an idea of what they were up against. When she found the first song to load, her mom opened the front door.

"Meg, I'm home."

"Okay."

"Did you clean your room?"

"Sure."

"I will be up to check it in a minute as soon as I put these groceries away."

Argh "Quick, you guys, hide!" *Wait, how do dust bunnies hide?* She recognized the fright in their eyes as they reverted to their original dust bunnies' form. *Oh, no.*

"Wait, Bunnies, can you change back?"

Sam crawled out from under the bed. "I am able to, as I am the most experienced one. The others haven't mastered the full technique yet."

Meg said, "Okay, Mom is coming up soon. So, can we gather up the gang the way they are now and stuff you all into the closet? She knows I throw everything behind that door in a big heap, so she never checks that mess."

"Yes, they will stick to one another in a long chain, and I can push them in between your things."

"Hurry it up, then." She opened the closet door and witnessed the cottontail pulling a string of furry balls behind him. She crammed them all in among her other plush animals.

"Pretend you are E.T. in there," she said, shutting the door in the confused rabbit's face.

Mom climbed the stairs, looked at the paperwork mess on the floor, and told Meg the room looked good. Apparently, she formed the idea that Meg had was attempting her homework and it thrilled her.

Meg released the rabbits from their warren. They resumed their discussions on their plan before bedtime and rehearsed the routine required to return to the closet while Meg attended class.

In the next few days, they reconfigured the bedroom to resemble that of the bandstand and stage area for the realism they needed to practice. Meg had meticulously recorded each song the class would sing during the musical spotlight in the play. Practice, practice, practice.

Sticks, the athletic bunny thumped her foot and hockey stick to the beat of the music. Another member of the training team, appropriately named Ringo, found a small wooden box and old soda can that he used as a drum and cymbal set. The rest of the bunnies stood in a chorus formation.

"Now we have it. Play the music again," said Sam.

Sam, acting as the director bunny, would continue that mantra, and Sticks thumped while Ringo drummed. Soon, every rabbit thumped and sang. The next thing they all knew, the vibration from the serious thudding jiggled Meg's two-foot round, purple piggy bank off her desk, smashing it to the floor. The coins from the bank flew everywhere.

"What was that crash I heard up there?" asked Mom.

"Um, things were shifting in my closet. I took care of it. Nothing to worry about, Mom."

"That girl and her mess." Her mom only shook her head and continued peeling the potatoes for dinner.

Two weeks before the play, Meg took the time out for a shopping trip. After purchasing the clothing she liked, buying a street vendor's lemonade, and gathering her courage, she made the eventual stop. She had to do it. She had faith this would work.

She spoke to the store manager, telling him what she wanted, and took him into her confidence. After a bit of haggling and a chuckle or two, they completed the deal.

"Not only shall I keep your confidence, young lady," he said behind a hand that covered up an ornery smile. "But I have to witness this to believe it."

This is going to make a dilly of a creative story for English. I can hardly wait.

With everything organized, all that remained were the final practice days. The MP3 player was no longer needed. By now, Meg and the rabbit chorus had memorized the songs.

The Night of the Play

That evening, Meg dressed in her regular school clothes. She and her mom entered the auditorium with Meg sitting on the aisle seat. As the lights dimmed, she requested permission to visit the restroom and slipped out.

The guitar and drummer had assembled on the right side of the choral group and began a slow prelude. The Master of Ceremonies spoke over the soft music and introduced the playwright, musical members, and their director to the audience. During the introductions, Meg's mom continued to gaze about, searching for Meg.

"Meg, where are you?" said the frustrated lady to herself.

Meanwhile, outside, Meg found the spot where her mom parked the van, crawled inside, and located the hidden items she needed.

The excited girl waited in the dark close to the stage doors, long enough for the play to begin. Then she snuck through the back door, slipped backstage, and hid behind stage props, waiting for her cue. In the van, she had changed her clothing into a white peasant blouse and a floor-length, flowing, black skirt with delicate, silver vertical threads running through it. She was ready with a professional performer's sparkle and confidence.

Oh, how I wish the bunnies were here.

"So, who said we aren't? There is dust everywhere, you know. We bunnies travel," said Sam.

"Are you nervous?" asked Sticks.

"Not on your life."

Building up from a slow intro to a fast beat, the duo guitar and drum performer began with "Summer of '69". Meg slowly entered stage left in her new ballet shoes, slipped to the side of the singers, and banged her hand on a tambourine adorned with black and silver ribbons. The audience gawked at the lone figure, as did the group on the risers while trying not to miss one downbeat in the music.

The medley of song chorus lines continued with "I Love Rock and Roll," "Eye of the Tiger," and "Billy Jean." By this time, one by one, the audience members rose to their feet, clapped to the beat, and sang along.

Fifteen minutes of popular '80s tunes continued. Meg remained in place, beat her tambourine with syncopated and professional style tambourine moves throughout the entire medley. She was in a dream world, and no one even dared make a move to stop her.

As the last song, "Power of Love" began, Meg gave the choral director a meaningful expression, turned, and left the stage.

This was so much fun. Musical talent doesn't always mean singing. Buying a tambourine was so worth my piggy bank money!

A TRUE FICTIONALIZED STORY.

"Summer of '69"	Bryan Adams
"I Love Rock and Roll"	Joan Jett and the Blackhearts
"Eye of the Tiger,"	Survivor
"Billy Jean"	Michael Jackson
"Power of Love"	Huey Lewis and the News

GRANDMA'S BUTTON BOX

AS IS MY TRADITION—A CHRISTMAS STORY

*H*ere at my grandmother's feet while she continued the ever-present hand sewing, I learned to count and sort. I arranged my colors and became skilled in hand-eye coordination by stringing buttons into a necklace, which I looped around my neck. As the fire crackled in the fireplace, Grams stitched. I would rest my head on her knee, watch the fire, and contemplate those questions about which only a small girl wondered.

Now, as I peered into her old button box, I saw such an unusual collection of items, realizing each held a special memory for her. *Why else would she have saved them in her button box? And why did we call it a button box if it was an old cookie tin?*

There were hairpins, not the bobby pins which have settled to the bottom of my make-up case, but the antique ones around which the delicate art of making hairpin lace was fashioned. The hairpins remained in the original container, and I knew these had once rattled around in that same box in the drawer of my great-grandmother's nightstand.

I held and rubbed a piece of a tiger's eye rock as if it were a worry stone. My grandmother loved being a rock-hound, and I remembered well the day I brought this one to her. I had been on a walk on the mega-hill by her house and found it lying on the road, a treasure waiting to be found. Obviously, it held a place in her heart.

Oh, an old eraser! I remembered the type that crumbled all over my papers when I tried to erase those pesky grade school math problems, normally ending with a hole in the page. And real wooden spools of thread. Did the colors not suit her or were these saved to make a future spool doll?

I recognized the corsage ribbon and pin nestled in the side curve of the tin from her 75th birthday bash where the band played on and on. Oh, what a memorable evening that turned out to be. She danced for hours. When it came time to make the thank-you speech she had planned, she became so overwhelmed as she looked out at the roomful of cheering family and friends; she stood silently frozen, unable to utter a sound.

There were buttons, big and small, metal buttons, Bakelite buttons, and some weird plastic buttons. I found a bone button (called underwear buttons in the

Civil War era). Buttons, buttons, buttons, and more buttons, a childhood delight! I ran my hands through them and enjoyed the clink, clink, clink of hearing them fall back into the metal cookie tin.

I looked back and remembered. Tears blurred my eyes, and I longed for those days when I sat at my grandmother's feet, watching the fire, and maybe listening to an old family tale.

Thinking of my button box, I located the tin and gently lifted it off the shelf. I knew the memories I would recall and took the time to travel that lane. There was and always will be a magical aura to a cookie tin with a new life as a button box. Clink, clink, clink, the buttons echoed the familiar sound as they sifted through my fingers, and I pondered who might one day contemplate its odd collection of items.

Christmas 2005

GRANNY ON A TRAPEZE

"*Y*ou want me to do what?" Granny moaned as she lifted another weight. "Lift these weights ten more times. Then, do that leg thingy?"

"That leg thingy is a 'leg press machine' and if you really want to fly the trapeze, you must have a powerful body. Plus, you haven't learned to hang onto the stationary bar," said Julie the young, perky, know-it-all instructor.

"But I only want to do it one time, to prove to myself that I can do it."

"Rules were rules, keep safety in mind. A first lesson is only the beginning, remember that, if you can."

Was she throwing sarcasm at her? Hmmm.

With a fist at her side, Granny cocked her hip and rolled her eyes. She was sixty-eight years young, five feet tall, her hair was untamed, a dark brown mess with a patch of solid white over her right eye. She liked to refer to it as the beginning of her skunk stripe. Her emerald-green eyes sparkled with anticipation anytime she spoke of this new adventure.

The vivid orange workout tights and purple jogging bra gave pause to the growing crowd of more athletic, younger trainees. Gawking at her had become a common pastime when the other athletes were not engaged in their own workouts and warmups.

"One… two… three..." Granny continued the arm curls using her weights. *Maybe it would have helped if she had told her why she wanted to be here in the first place. Nah, it wouldn't have mattered to Julie. Rules were rules!* Her mind flew back to how this adventure had begun. She shook her head and hoped her brilliant idea actually worked.

The following two Saturdays were the second and third lessons, and the old gal continued to argue with Julie about flying. "Just let me try it and get this done," she begged her teacher, hoping to put this *'brilliant idea' in her rear-view mirror. Obviously, her nerves had nearly won over her willpower.*

To Granny, if this petite pony-tailed Princess of Evil had dropped the rope ladder down and allowed her to climb up, she would have finished this exercise nonsense and gone straight to the heart of this project. Julie was not mean to Granny, only demanding. Young adults didn't always compute that they should handle older adults with a generous amount of delicate, kid-gloved care. Where patience and understanding of the more mature client worked well, demanding attitudes did not, especially with Granny.

"Stationary bar next. Jump up, grab the bar, and hold yourself up for twenty seconds. You don't need to do a pull-up, only hang there," Julie instructed. "If you can manage to pull your legs through, and hang by your knees, that is a plus but not mandatory at this point."

"Well, that wasn't so hard," Granny said as she flashed a mischievous smile to The Princess.

"That is because you've been concentrating on strength training, which is so important in older adults. Next week is your fourth week, and you may try your skills," Julie replied.

Granny drove home, full of relief now that she could see the end of this adventure in sight, but her irritation about the older adult remark remained a stinging bite.

"Today was a tough one," she said to her teenage neighbor as she slithered out of her Camaro onto the ground. She just lay there, too exhausted to do more than wave at him.

"Oh, surely you jest," Tucker teased as he looked down at her. He loved to poke fun at her about her brilliant ideas. Mostly, though, he liked to wait for her to come home so he could visit his dream car.

Granny loved that Z-28 convertible. She owned a muscle car in pristine condition from back in the day. She was forever polishing the white paint, cleaning the red upholstery, or taking it in for checkups.

Tucker liked to put the top down and ride to town with her. They both laughed when they saw the reflective streak of white in the shop windows as they drove by. Granny's father used to call it the Flying Bathtub. Tucker would sit up straight, blast the radio, and hang his arm over the side. His shaggy black hair blew in the wind, and those brown eyes glowed with delight as they came to a stoplight.

He prodded Granny to gun the engine. The startled looks the other drivers gave her were so worth it. This gutsy old lady had it going on. His mom would ground him for sure if he knew what they were doing on her errand days. Granny could even do a 180-reverse turnaround by yanking up the emergency brake and spinning the steering wheel into a power slide. She only did this if no one appeared to be watching, and they never ever would tell Mom about it.

Four weeks earlier

"ONE DAY I AM GOING TO HAVE A CAR EXACTLY LIKE this one," Tucker repeated this same phrase every time they had been out joyriding or working on the car.

"I told you, dreaming is good, but you have to work hard to make your dreams come true. What are you willing to do to make them happen?" Granny wanted a sincere answer and wouldn't stop nagging him until she received one.

"I have no clue. School is so boring. The only class I really like is Art. There is a city art contest in a few weeks which I would like to enter, but I'm too scared to try. Afraid I'll fail."

"What! … Fail? … What kind of an attitude is that?"

"I just can't do it. What we do in school is so lame. Our teacher is so old. All he has us do are these dumb landscapes. I like to draw architectural buildings," Tucker said. "Old people don't understand how it is."

"I beg your pardon! Old people? Old people?" Granny sputtered, adding an eyeball roll as they walked up the steps to their porches for the night. "Is it an actual fear which you need to conquer or is it something you use for an excuse, so you won't have to do it? Think about that. Don't let this opportunity pass you by."

"That was a real 'old person' fireball bit of inspiration." Tucker laughed from across the yard.

Her young friend was right. She gave an older person's advice, but did she even practice what she preached? After a sleepless night, Granny hit upon what was a truly inspirational idea. Convincing Tucker would be the problem. *Convincing herself would be no simple task, either.*

She thought it over for a few days before she approached him with her idea.

"Tucker, I had the idea of the year... I have a GBI... a Granny's Brilliant Idea."

"Oh, no, not another one. The executive committee in her mind was at it again."

"Okay, here it is. Did I ever tell you I am terrified of heights?"

"Wait, what, YOU? No way, never, you have never been afraid of anything."

"Not true. All heights have terrified me. I can't even wear high heels. I had this thought, though. Since you have been afraid to enter the art contest, and I am afraid of high places, what if I made a deal with you?"

"Oh, ya, like what?" he asked, a bit on the suspicious side. He never knew what Granny would dream up in that head of hers.

"We both face our fears. I would take flying trapeze lessons if you entered the art contest," Granny said as nonchalantly as she could. "I want to know what it feels like to fly the trapeze. And, I am positively terrified, pinky swear terrified to try it. I'll let you drive the Camaro, if you compete in the contest, not just enter it, actually compete. So... would you be up for it?"

"What! The trapeze?" he howled, slapping his side while he burst forth with a deep belly laugh.

"Seriously? Give me time to think about it." He ran his hand through his floppy mane of hair, thinking less than a minute. He said, "Wait, did you say I could drive the Camaro?" Then, pausing only a second, he took a deep breath and eagerly said, "Okay, I will."

Saturday morning both fraidy-cats filled out forms for their parts in the bargain. Granny began biting her nails and pacing. It would be an entire week before she started her lessons.

Meanwhile, returning home, Tucker immediately launched into his project. He smiled to himself as he mentally planned out his artwork. He appeared excited, Granny on the other hand was a nervous wreck.

AFTER THE FOURTH LESSON, THE ANTICIPATED FLYING day arrived.

After Julie said her colorful student could fly, Granny invited Tucker to drive with her to the graduation day in the Camaro. He carried his camera with him and decided he would upload Granny's adventure to YouTube, but he wasn't about to tell her that.

Granny warmed up with her stretches. As Julie coached, she went to the rope ladder. She climbed eight steps, then her right leg slipped through the metal horizontal step of the ladder. She flew backward, holding onto the side rope with her right hand. Her left arm swung backward, waving in a wide arc, and her left knee hit the rung above the one she had originally been standing upon. Her feet cycled the air before she found her footing.

She grabbed ahold of the rung above her, righted herself, and began the journey again. This time she went twelve more steps and looked down. Big mistake. She grabbed onto the lifeline with both hands and wouldn't move. A wobble and sway of the climbing system began, which she determined wasn't from a breeze but from her trembling. Twenty-four feet above the ground looked more like a view from the moon.

Julie said, "You made it, Granny."

Down below was dead silence as the other students watched with either horror or admiration.

"I can't move, I can't move," Granny moaned.

"Come back down Granny. If you're scared, you don't have to do it. It's okay. I understand," Tucker coaxed.

"I will NOT GIVE UP," Granny yelled, but still, she couldn't move.

"Give me your hand, I'll help you," Julie said. "One more step, and you'll be on the boards."

Granny stuck her head through the ladder rungs and closed her eyes. The world was spinning. She knew she would fall. She couldn't breathe. Her heart was thumping. She looked down again and saw her friend's frightened face.

Tucker, indeed, feared she would hang herself with her head between the ladder rungs, or she would tremble so hard she would fall.

"Why do I keep looking down?" she moaned.

"Granny come down, come down."

"Granny come up, come up."

"EVERYONE… BE… QUIET!" she screamed and

closed her eyes one more time. Then she slowly opened them. She took a deep breath. Her hands shook as she loosened her left-hand grip, maintaining a firm hold with her right, and let go of the metal rung she'd been grasping.

"Get back, Julie, I am doing this myself or not at all," she said as she moved at a snail's pace, pulling herself onto the boards above her head. She didn't stand up, but instead, she laid herself flat on them.

A slight breeze blew the wind flags.

Julie stood to the side on the standing boards, watching the progress. The determined lady had a safety harness on, so Julie knew Granny was safe, but she had never been this worried for a student. The air was deathly quiet.

After a few moments, Julie said, "Granny, what are you doing?"

Through gritted teeth, Granny replied, "What do you think I'm doing? I'm sacrificing myself to the trapeze gods."

The feisty senior eventually pulled herself to a sitting position on the platform and while holding the side mounting system, inched upward until she was standing. Her knees were shaking, her hands slippery, and her hair soaked to the skin with sweat. This time, she did not look down. Apparently, the trapeze gods were in good humor today. No sacrifice required.

Angelo, another aerial artist, sat across the net on his platform, waiting patiently and quietly for the drama to continue. *Would she fly or not? Did she have the courage?*

Julie gave her a wink of encouragement and reminded her to 'chalk up' so her hands would not slip on the metal rod. Before handing her the bar, she said, "You've got this. Remember to keep your arms stiff and your body straight, pump with your legs together like you were on a swing. You only have to hold on as long as you want, fly, and then drop." Tucker's heart beat like a bass drum. His mouth turned dry, and his hands quivered as he tried to snap off a picture. No one had ever made such a sacrifice for him, but it had been her dream, and he wanted it for this brave lady.

Granny's weathered hands grabbed the bar. Someone yelled, "Ready... hep." She closed her eyes, jumped straight up, and out into the air she went. She pumped her legs hard and went back and forth, higher, and higher. To everyone's surprise, laughter bubbled from her with each pass.

"Wahoo," she yelled with a wide grin plastered across her face. She let go of the bar with a perfect back flop into the net. She had flown the trapeze!

She never heard the whoops below or the congratulations from the other students. She did vaguely remember hearing Julie yell something about upcoming classes. Granny glowed in her own aura while Tucker babbled on and on. No words would express how she felt.

Tucker's turn.

Tucker's art contest was the next weekend. His mom and favorite neighbor were there. If he was nervous, it didn't show. He did his best and enjoyed the challenge. Before the doors opened to the guests, the judges viewed the entries and pinned ribbons in places of honor.

The visitors were eager to see the results. When at last they could see Tucker's project, Granny was stunned. This was NOT what she expected. Not one bit. *This was awful. Were people to live like moles and birds?* She expected a skyscraper or apartments or a building since he had said he liked the architectural design. His creation sure did not win the Best in Show, far from it. Nor did it even place in any category.

Oh, what had she done? How would she console the boy? Or his mom?

The artist didn't appear to be the least bit distressed. He was talking to an animated man with long hair who wore formal clothing. The man gestured at the exhibits, and they both laughed.

What in the world could make him laugh after this disaster of a project?

Tucker eventually made his way to his two guests. The gentleman he had been talking to had earned the position of student recruiter for the Art Institute across town and wished to interview Tucker for a spot in next year's class. Plus, since there had been so much interest from the crowd in his project, the recruiter felt he had a better-than-average chance of winning a scholarship to the institute, should he wish to submit a portfolio of his designs.

Tucker explained, "People liked it because of the futuristic design. It is a view of what buildings would look like on planets such as ours, both above and below ground. I used star cluster graffiti hanging from the sky as a backdrop to highlight the idea of outer space. I think mixing it together attracted their attention. It was not art by old people's standards."

"*Again, with the old people?*"

"I guess we both learned a bit about conquering our fears, didn't we?" said Granny. "Look what we would have missed if we hadn't tried."

"How about if you drive me home in the Camaro tonight if it is okay with your mom?" Granny offered and dangled the keys in front of Tucker.

Mom smiled and nodded. "I know you two won't get into any mischief if you are together."

Both Tucker and Granny just smiled at one another.

The boy's eyes lit up. It may not fulfill the dream of owning a car like it but driving the muscle car made him a winner today.

As they drove home, Granny had suggested they take the scenic route, so they would have more time for discussion, and Tucker would have more time behind the wheel. She had an idea in mind which she had been mulling over for some time now and needed an opinion.

"Now, Tucker, I've been thinking. I'm wondering what it would be like to be a roller derby girl and fly around the track."

Again, with the flying thing? Well, at least her feet would be on the ground.

2018—Moline, Illinois

Addendum: This is not a true story. It is a wish story. There was a Camaro in my history, though. I always said when I turned seventy, I was going to take lessons on how to fly the trapeze. Research is complete. The school is in Chicago. I am now seventy-one (2021). Courage and fear of heights are the problems.

HIGH SCHOOL LOVE

My heart soars as those eyes gently caress me.
Unto me, happiness has fallen.
In a single moment, life has dealt a blessing, one which
neither can explain.
Come, hold me in your arms, let my weakness find
strength in your touch.
Let me know this is real, where no falseness lies, no
insincerity, no reason to doubt.
For within these gentle moments, a love is born and
grown.
The future unknown, the past a memory, this moment is
ours.
If I never have another dream, let this be the only one I
will ever need.

Colorado Springs, Colorado 1968

LOVE THY NEIGHBOR

MY ANNUAL CHRISTMAS STORY

*I*t would be like any other Halloween, or so I thought, me in my witch's costume, kids at the ready with candy bags in hand impatiently waiting for the right shade of dark. Then, the phone rang with my neighbor's grown daughter in quite a frazzle on the other end of the line.

"I must step out for a bit, but I can't leave Mom alone. Could you please run over and stay with her?" I found this a strange request from a neighbor who had lived next door to our family for several years, yet whom I barely knew.

"Well, I guess," I said. "But I am wearing a costume." (As if that should make any difference.)

"Mom will love it, please do come."

I sent the children off to trick or treat, and I ran next door. I had heard Mary, my neighbor, had been ill, but there was no way I could have prepared myself for what I was about to see.

The daughter met me at the door with her coat over her arm and took me to Mary's room, saying, "Everything will be fine. I'll only pick up a few items and return in a short while. Just don't let any bubbles get in the line."

Huh? Now don't let any bubbles get in the line? What in the world? As I crossed the threshold to Mary's bedroom, I stopped dead in my tracks, mouth agape, heart racing, and feeling foolish wearing theatrical make-up and this so out-of-place witch's costume.

There lay my neighbor, hooked up to a medical machine, and unable to speak. But laugh, how she laughed. Her entire body shook as she stared at me and then laughed some more. *I saw no humor in this situation.*

As I tried to regain my composure, I followed her daughter to the door. She *then* explained to me that her mom had Lou Gehrig's disease, was diagnosed as terminal, could not speak, and required constant care.

Oh, great, and she is leaving me in charge? Me, of all people. Nurse Nancy, I never pretended to be.

"Just don't let any air bubbles go up the line," she repeated to me like I surely didn't hear her the first time.

I poked my made-up face back in the bedroom doorway. Once again, the bedridden lady flew into gales of laughter. She sure had a great sense of humor, and since she couldn't speak, we certainly made an odd couple

69

trying to communicate. I talked to her, read to her, and watched tv with her. During the entire visit, I continued a running commentary. Any topic was fair game.

Deep in the recesses of my mind, I remembered I must check her machine. What it did, I didn't know other than to help Mary's breathing. But I knew it was a medical marvel of great importance. And of course, as luck would have it, what did I see, but air bubbles inching up that clear tubing. *Tiny bubbles, little bubbles. . .*

At that point, I must have been quite a sight hopping about the room from one side of her bed to the other, croaking out the words, "Mary, Mary, there are bubbles in the line, what should I do?" *(Like she was going to talk to me.)*

And, for crying out loud, she went into fits of laughter again.

How could she think this was funny when her very life was in my hands? This was no time for laughter. Mary had a limited capacity for movement, but she reached over, gave that line a flip, and POOF, bubbles gone. All was fine. . . except for me, of course.

From that point on, our strange friendship began. Whenever the family needed help, they called on me. Apparently, my costumed visit had been a hit, and since I had acquired quite a collection of costumes over the years, I always showed up in a strange manner of dress. I learned how to communicate with her, help care for her physical needs, keep her laughing, and love a stranger.

In her last days, when Mary was confined to the hospital, I received the call.

"Would you put the clown costume on one more time?"

I arrived at the hospital, appearing in my clown costume as requested. The room was filled with family members. The space around her sleeping form echoed with teasing me on my appearance and the retelling of family stories.

I pleaded with Mary, "Mary, please wake up and help me with this joking family of yours." Then…. a tiny miracle happened, she opened her eyes, smiled at me, and closed them once more.

I so grieved the passing of that lady. Yes, because a life had been taken from us, but more so because she was a wonderful lady whom I never had taken the time to know.

My friends, if you can't take the time to love thy neighbor, at least take the time to know thy neighbor.

Christmas 2002

MOUNTAIN HIKE

*T*he mountain air felt crisp. The hillside glittered with specks of fool's gold, and the pebbles were begging to be kicked. The slight rustle to the dying aspen leaves mimicked that of crumpling, wrapping paper. A perfect morning for a mountain hike with my best friend, Becky. Even a cottontail rabbit with black-tipped ears skittered across our path and ventured out for a romp in the sun.

We were typical teenagers in our tye-died T-shirts, flowered triangle headscarves, and frayed cutoff jeans. I liked to wear my pink swirled T-shirt, big and loose. Becky wore a vibrant red one, a size too small if one looked closely.

Becky had sun-streaked blonde hair that naturally flipped up at the tips. My dark brunette hair looked like scarecrow straw, so I always requested it to be cut in a pixie style, as it wouldn't hold a curl for anything. Becky favored black mascara and a foundation tint matching her fair skin. I had big green eyes, no mascara, and freckles sprinkled across my nose. I felt fortunate that my parents even let me wear pale lipstick. We both wore our favorite baby pink nail polish. One thing I had was pretty legs. I worshiped the sun to make sure they remained bronzed. Day in and day out, I offered myself to the sun gods to rotate like a chicken on a spit to maintain that golden look.

We gossiped about who deserved our vote for Homecoming King and Queen. Mary and Ken had my vote because they were always so nice to everyone. Becky rather liked the stuck-up couple. I believe she disagreed with me for the sake of disagreement. That stuck-up couple wouldn't give her the time of day. If you didn't belong in their clique, you didn't matter.

As we kicked rocks to see which one would skip the farthest, we had a 'just for fun' contest to see which of Peter, Paul, and Mary's songs was the best, "Puff the Magic Dragon" or "Blowin' in the Wind?" Whichever rock went the farthest would win. No one won. They both went the same distance, and we laughed at our silliness.

Meanwhile, I belted out "Puff, the magic dragon lived by"... It came out like a frog croaking, as I couldn't carry a tune in a bucket. I didn't care if anyone heard me. I loved to sing.

It didn't matter though, as Becky sang over the top of me with "How many roads must a man… " Becky would show off her trained voice at any opportunity. And this time was no exception.

She always wanted to be the best at everything. I wondered why we are even friends.

We both agreed on Bobby Vinton's "Blue Velvet" as being gush worthy. What a dreamboat with those piercing blue eyes and that black leather jacket. We always talked about the cute guys we wish would look our way but realistically knew they never would.

With every step we took, dust flew up and stuck to my freshly lotioned legs. My white sneakers were turning saddle color brown. We followed the trail as it wound around the hillside. I could hear loose pebbles bouncing off the side of the trail as we climbed higher. We were turning at a bend in the trail as I caught a flash of something moving toward us.

"Run!" I let out a blood-curdling scream.

"What?" Becky jumped and screamed because I screamed.

"I said run, something is out there!" I grabbed the tail of her T-shirt in a bunch as I ran by while urging her to move. Her hair was flying straight out as I whipped her around.

Tony skidded down off the hillside shadows laughing at us.

"That was so good," he roared. "I could hear you

two a mile away. Such easy targets. I knew you were ripe for a good fright, only had to wait you out."

Becky whirled around, fluttering her hands in frustration.

"Oh, hi, Tony. You nearly scared the wits out of Annie," Becky said, smoothing out her shirt, then her hair, trying to cover up her own fright. "What are you doing out here?" she asked.

"Going hunting for waskly wabbits," he quipped his imitation of Elmer Fudd and watched to see our reaction. I smiled. Becky only stared.

Tony was Becky's cute neighbor.

"Do you want to walk with us?" Becky asked as she moved close enough to him to brush the hair from out of his eyes. Becky wiggled an opening between me and Tony, not on the other side of him, between us. He shouldered his rifle, and the three of us continued on our way.

He frowned at this and pushed her hand aside. To him, this was a stroll down a mountain path, not a rugged hike.

I had a serious crush on Tony, but I didn't dare tell anybody. Not even Becky was aware of it, and I told her everything. I hoped my excitement had not become obvious; the heat of my blush might give me away. Needing to do something with my nervous hands, I feathered my pixie bangs on my forehead and covered the beginning of a grin with my hand.

"I will only go a short way with you. I really have more important things to do other than spend the afternoon walking with two girls," he smirked. "What kind of hike could you be taking; you aren't even wearing hiking boots?"

And then it happened. "Umph," I groaned as I splatted face down on the ground, arms splayed to the side like a frog. I had stumbled over my own feet as I tried to adjust my shorter steps to their long ones.

"Clumsy," Becky chided.

Tony offered me a hand up. He gave me a crooked smile that totally took my breath away. As he did so, his long hair flopped over his forehead into his eyes again. Even though long hair was stylish, Tony's mop of black hair needed a trim. But when he brushed it off his face, it was those piercing blue eyes that made me sigh. He was *my* version of Bobby Vinton.

He was tall and rugged with the body of a back-woodsman. I imagined chopping wood and hunting wildlife in the forest helped to build up that well-muscled body. Unlike a man of the woods, he didn't wear flannel; he wore black. Everything was black, even his jeans. Black.

Tony was a year older than us. He lived two houses down on Becky's side of the street. I could see where he lived from my house. My house was across the street from Becky's but from my window, I could see Tony's place.

His dark, shuttered, white cottage set back from the

street on a gravel drive. The front yard where grass normally would grow showed an unkept bare dirt yard. Several towering blue spruce trees, and from the look of it, a lack of interest in gardening, shut it off from the road and sun. Surrounding the rest of the yard stood a six-foot-high wooden fence. A wire gate the width of the driveway closed in the front entrance. Planted firmly in that bare patch of ground, a NO SOLICITING sign remained as a semi-warning.

Often, I could see Tony opening or closing the driveway gate as different cars came and went.

Was it my imagination that he looked around to see if anyone was watching? In a flash, I would dive under the windowsill, nearly knocking myself out, hoping he didn't have supervision and hadn't seen me. No one actually knew his family. On rare occasions, I could hear heated, foreign-accented voices.

We three walked for a half-hour, then sidestepped down a slope to a lush level meadow below. Sitting in the sunshine with a slight wind from the quaking aspens made for a perfect afternoon.

"Would you like half of my candy bar?" I asked Tony.

"Sure."

I hoped my hand didn't shake as Tony touched it when I passed it over to him. The sway of the grass was mesmerizing. Lupine and wild columbines poked up sporadically in the field.

I squinted hard, and I knew I saw a rabbit nibbling

on the field grass. That bunny had the same black tips on his ears as the one this morning.

"Do you think that could be the same bunny we saw earlier, the one with the black-tipped ears?" I asked.

"This is the dumbest thing you have said all day. How could you even think that rabbit would manage to hop all the way over here?" Becky rolled her eyes as she laughed at me.

Once again, I was feeling my face warm. Now she had frightened the rabbit with her outburst, and he had loped away.

If she had seen the rabbit, I am sure it would have been an all-important event. I sucked in a breath and tried to ignore her. Making a big deal of this would ruin the day, so I let her rude remarks pass by. At the same moment Becky laughed, I glanced at Tony in time to see the tightening of his jaw muscles.

Had he seen my embarrassment? I hoped not.

He changed the subject by telling us about how he often hunted rabbits for family dinners. I found this interesting, as the men in my family were not hunters.

"How did you learn to hunt?" I quickly asked.

"What do you do with the fur?"

"Don't you feel bad shooting those cute rabbits?"

"Do you have a lucky rabbit's foot?"

"Geez, Annie take a breath," Becky said. But I kept on asking questions.

"What does rabbit taste like?"

I rapid-fired my questions at him as I hoped they

covered my nerves, changed the subject, and would shut Becky up for the time being if Tony took the time to answer.

He explained his father taught him to hunt when he was much younger. He told us his mother cooked the rabbit with special spices like rosemary and sage, or it would taste 'gamey' whatever the heck that meant. I didn't want to appear any dumber, so I didn't bother to ask that question. Becky sat flicking the polish off her fingernails and remained unusually silent.

The sun shone directly overhead. The shimmery ball of orange, warm rays on an endless sky of azure blue felt warm and inviting sitting in that meadow.

"You know that guy, Dennis, in Mr. Fiero's class? He is in detention for the third time," I said.

"I told Dennis if he quit smoking those Camels in the bathroom, detention wouldn't be such a big part of his life," Tony told us. "Then the idiot asked me for my lighter."

We hooted about that one. We passed the rest of the time talking about our worst teachers ever and telling jokes.

Tony sat between us and occasionally took a liberty with a hand on my well-shaved, tanned leg, or a brush on Becky's breast. All along, he had shown disdain for girls, and especially Becky's fawning ways. Now he seemed to flip his attitude. This was totally unacceptable to me.

My heart thumped an extra beat as I took in a sharp

breath. Becky appeared to enjoy that sort of attention. She flipped her hair, giggled, and gave him an obvious wink when he favored her with this sort of attention. What exactly went through his mind?

None of his actions appeared to bother Becky. For some time, I had felt suspicious about my friend's knowledge and experience with boys. She knew too much about kissing and getting to second base. I wondered if she needed more attention or needed to be the center OF attention.

It surprised me to think about Tony's unexpected behavior. I was so naïve, and I had not taken the time to think beyond handsome good looks and what being alone with a boy in the woods might mean.

Would he risk trying out 'the bases' with us? I had to wonder, did he move his leg, so it was closer to mine? Had his arm always been behind me when I had leaned backward? Was my imagination playing tricks on me, or could I really feel his breath on my neck?

I remained curious yet still uncomfortable in this area of boy-girl relationships. I had already experienced my first kiss at the after-school sock hop. Right after "Blue Velvet." It was so quick, and the guy's dry, chapped lips barely touched mine. I could not even call it romantic. Not what I would have expected a first kiss to be. But what we had here could turn way beyond anything I had learned so far in the girl's locker room.

I felt we were in awkward, uncomfortable territory,

and I knew it was a good time to leave. Noticing the trees were casting shadows, I stood and brushed off stray pieces of grass and dirt. Becky scowled at me as she realized it was my intention to start for home.

"Oh, of course, this about figures," she whispered to me with irritation as she stood and moved closer to me. With no other option but to go along, she stood and commanded us to hurry.

She started up the slope ahead of Tony and me. I continued babbling. "The downhill slide was much easier than going back up this hill," I puffed out the words.

We bent forward on the upward climb, working to catch up to Becky. We stopped for a moment so I could catch my breath.

"Oh, you are such a great mountain girl. You need way more training," Tony teased, as he noted my lack of hiking skills.

I guessed it was his way to help pass away the previous awkward moments.

On the top of the hill, the queen stood, arms crossed, tapping her foot. *Oh, I knew that look.* She was steaming mad. She obviously had overheard Tony's words.

"Oh, come on. Who is going to train her? You?" she hissed as she slapped her hand to her side. She looked like a tigress, ready to strike. The lack of attention on her certainly showed in her present attitude.

As my breathing returned to normal, I glanced to my

right. I was struck speechless by what I saw. Tony's lips pressed into a tight line. Those same blue eyes that had earlier been so beautiful to me now looked menacing. My eyes widened in shock as Tony slipped the rifle from his shoulder, took careful aim, and shot Becky.

Colorado Springs, Colorado Fall 1964

MR. WHISKERS DID WHAT?

"$\mathcal{W}$ait till you see the hippo exhibit," the limping older gentleman chuckled to the visitors who were entering the front door as he left. "Our zoo certainly knows how to entertain."

"This way, this way, follow me, young man, you come over here this minute!" His aunt called out. She needed a herding dog as she wrangled her nephew and birthday guests forward. Trying to pass around the rowdy party group, curious patrons became part of the existing crowd and followed along to see what was so exciting at the hippo exhibit.

Mr. Whiskers, the resident hippopotamus, had been enjoying his day in the hippo pond. The community raised the funds and constructed the habitat, especially for him, with water several feet deep in his pond. A field-sized grassland enclosed the area, surrounding the prairie-like home.

He was one special dude. The zoo had previously run a public contest to name him. Hippopotamus meant River Horse. The zoo judges wanted him to be identified by an unusual name, not the common entry of The River Horse, so Mr. Whiskers won his name because of the whiskers on his chin. All hippos had them, not only boy hippos. His popularity proved to be wonderful for the zoo, and he soon became the zoo mascot. The zoo artists designed T-shirts for the gift shop with his tooth-filled, smiling face decorating the front.

The pond was deep enough that he could take a soothing soak for his massive body or sink to the bottom and hold his breath for up to seven minutes any time he wished. Hippos can't swim but they had the ability to walk along the bottom of a pond or river while holding their breath. Mr. Whiskers never had an earache because his nose and ears closed when he played "hide the hippo" and sunk to the bottom of his pond.

When his underwater time was up, he whooshed straight up, making a tsunami of waves onto his playground. He timed it perfectly, as the children had little patience when it involved waiting for him to surface. This hippo loved to perform for his guests. Mr. Whiskers wiggled his tiny ears at them. Or he opened his mouth in a three-foot-wide yawn. His mouth was so big his friend Nigel, the penguin, could stand inside if he wanted to, but why would Nigel even dream of doing such a dumb thing?

This river horse weighed close to six thousand pounds. When he showed off his dancing, the children laughed and clapped. His version of The Twist delighted anyone who witnessed it.

Every Friday afternoon a four-foot-tall girl peered through the glass at the hippo enclosure. A smiling gray-haired lady with dazzling blue eyes who wore workout clothes, and a snow parka held the child's hand.

The girl acted exactly in an opposite manner of her older companion. She never smiled. Everyone smiled when they saw the zoo mascot. What could be the trouble with this little girl? A mystery for sure.

Mr. Whiskers named the child the Little Pink Girl. She wore fur topped, pink boots, a pink wool coat, and a pink, sparkly, knitted hat, which she continued to wear every week. Scarecrow-like tufts of dark hair stuck out of her bonnet. Her eyes were the color of tropical green water. Mr. Whiskers imagined her heart-shaped mouth at one time had been so adorable when she smiled.

Mr. Whiskers now had a mission. He determined it was his duty as an entertainer to help her smile and laugh. From what Tina, his trainer reported, Little Pink Girl's mama was in Europe for the next several months finishing up her work. Her grandma took care of her.

Mr. Whiskers knew in his heart that laughter would help her. So, he tried blowing bubbles out of his big mouth at her. It didn't work. He made his honking noise to talk to her. It didn't work.

He wiggled his ears while he looked right into her eyes. Nope. One week, he climbed out of his warm water bath and performed his Twist dance. He bellowed at Tina to cue up the music to "Twist and Shout." That one never failed him. Fail it did. *Oh fine, fine, now what am I to do?*

Tina's Aunt Beth and her friend knew this was a popular venue at the zoo. On their lady's day out, they were frequent visitors to Tina's workplace. When Mr. Whiskers spied them and the mega shoulder bag that they each carried, his cavern of a mouth opened in an excited hello greeting. He had spied what those bags held.

Wait, wait, he had it. There it was the idea that would make Little Pink Girl smile. Later, he would talk to Tina.

"Tina, Tina," he honked out to her in his hippo language, which, of course, Tina understood. After all, she was his trainer. Every day she gave him the sign to open his mouth to receive a head of lettuce, and as her treat for feeding him, he taught her a new word. She understood his "hippo talk" quite well now.

"Would you speak to your aunt and her friend for me? I had an idea. This is what I would like them to do." Mr. Whiskers described his plan.

"You are the craziest hippo I have ever known. You want them to do what?" Tina asked.

"I am the **ONLY** hippo you have ever known." He reminded her of that fact as he rolled his eyes.

Being the best friend to her hippo and wanting to please him, Tina asked Aunt Beth and her companion to return to the zoo. They both agreed to do so.

The following day, the two ladies scurried to the workroom behind the hippo enclosure. Aunt Beth took out a pad and pencil from her tote bag. She continued to make notes while Tina explained the detailed plan.

"This is going to be so much fun." The friends giggled. "Give us two weeks." They chattered like chipmunks as they left the workroom.

Two weeks later, that Friday afternoon was like any other Friday. Little Pink Girl came to visit Mr. Whiskers with her grandmother. They stood together with the crowd facing the viewing window. Grandmother's eyes opened wide as she covered her mouth with a gloved hand.

As normal, Little Pink Girl peeked through the window at the hippo, then down at her fur-lined boots, shaking her head. She looked up again and gawked at Mr. Whiskers.

"Grandma?"

She inhaled a huge breath and from her pixie mouth, a roar of laughter erupted. The little miss slapped her leg and doubled over, holding her tummy. Little Pink Girl laughed so hard her sides hurt.

"Grandma, did you see that?"

Guests could hear her burbling laughter from several exhibits over and rushed forward to see what was causing the uproar. Indeed, there was excitement in the house today. The zoo's "crowd-control employees" scurried to the event to stop the pushing, or people would be squished.

Inside the hippo's world was Mr. Whiskers floating in his pond on a pink inner tube. He wore a knitted bonnet and a hula skirt. His bonnet was like the one Little Pink Girl wore. It was pink with sparkly glitter exactly like hers. Tina's aunt and her friend had knitted Mr. Whiskers a bonnet! He spied their knitting needles and yarn in the shoulder bags they carried when they last visited Tina, and his idea was born.

Tina turned up the familiar Twist music and the famous hippo flopped himself off the inner tube into the water and wiggled out of the pond. He began his Twist dance, honking his hippo voice to the music. The water drops flew on the rocks, the walls, and straight to the window as his hula skirt twirled out around him.

Mr. Whiskers waddled up to the glass window, winked at the laughing girl, opened his mouth wide, and hippo roared a hello. The teeth in the open hippo's mouth looked like miniature tree stumps.

"I don't believe this, Grandma. I have never seen anything so funny in my whole life. Wait till I tell Mama."

Mr. Whiskers was so thrilled. The child turned to wave as they walked away. She was still giggling. He knew laughter would help to heal her loneliness, and he felt in his heart that she would be back. Hippos live up to forty years so he knew he would see her peeking through the window a lot.

Summer 2019

NOODLE ME

CHICKEN & NOODLES (FOR FOUR HUNGRY PEOPLE)

*M*y paternal grandmother undertook the task of teaching me to cook and sew at an early age. The following is a family recipe that she taught me to make when I was only ten years old. The instructions are written <u>exactly</u> as she instructed me. This being the only way a young child could remember them. She continued to teach my children in the same manner.

This is what she would say:

We need one gigantic bowl for one small child.

An absolutely bare countertop is important.

Find the rolling pin or a smooth pop bottle (sometimes you must learn how to improvise and ridges on pop bottles do not roll noodles out flat).

Look for the gigantic, big pot for cooking.

Now line up these ingredients: a whole store-bought

chicken, two eggs, water, baking powder, and salt. Do not name the chicken.

Boil the chicken in the pot. (Grams must do this) First, take out the inside stuffing guts if it is a whole chicken. (Laugh if you must, but I have forgotten this step several times.) Your broth will be yucky if you do not remember this step.

Next, the child must stand on a chair to be tall enough to reach the counter. Look for the oversized apron in the drawer. Tie it around the child, tie up hair, if necessary.

In the gigantic bowl put in the two eggs, stir really, really fast with a fork. Save the eggshells. Fill one half of an eggshell with water, add to the eggs–the water–not the eggshell. Then take your thumb and jam it into the can of baking powder and come up with a thumbnail of baking powder. Dump it into the eggs and water. (If you use baking soda, your noodles will look rather greenish. . . yuk again). Add the same amount of salt, only this time the technique is to pour the salt into your cupped hand. Guessing works well at this point. You know, 'guess this is about right.'

Mix really, really fast with the fork again.

Now, pull out the flour can from beside the old stove. (Our family had a giant-size one the children would sit on as an extra seat in the kitchen when we had company. I can still remember, "Grams, Grams, can I sit on the flour can?" It was a place of honor.)

From the flour can, dip out the flour, start with about

a handful, only you really must use the scooper. Some will fall on the floor, but that is okay. We can sweep later. Mix the flour into the egg stuff. Keep adding more flour until the dough is stiff. (Note: I said bare countertop earlier.) Spread more flour all over the counter, then turn the bowl upside down and plop out the dough from the bowl. The flour on the countertop will fly all over the kitchen and the child. That was always the fun part. Grams always laughed. Use the rolling pin or smooth bottle to roll out the noodles nice and flat.

Disagreement

Here we always, always disagreed. She was from the old school and insisted the noodles be rolled out very, very thin. I, on the other hand, being of sound mind and opinion insisted over the years, and still do that noodles need to be fat. You may be your own judge here with no arguments from the writer (meaning me, the granddaughter).

Once the noodles are rolled out flat and do not stick to the counter... (should this happen, scrape them off the counter), add more flour and re-roll them. Then roll the noodles up jelly-roll fashion, continuing to add flour to the inside of the roll.

Use a sharp knife to cut the noodles. Grams does this one, too.

Meanwhile, back to the chicken in the pot. It should be finished boiling by now. Take it out of the broth.

Save the broth. To the broth, you may add a plop of butter, one or two chicken bouillon cubes, and salt if you do not feel it is flavorful enough. Turn off the burner.

Rip up the chicken and tear it into tiny pieces. You may want to let that hot chick cool first. Remember, Grams said not to name the chicken, it will be too hard to part with it if you did. My grandparents were farm folks, so naming animals you intended to eat was not considered a wise thing to do.

Now, the broth on the stove should be turned back on and brought to a boil. (That is after the noodles are cut, and the chicken is in pieces) Once the broth is boiling, put the ripped-up chicken back in the broth. Add the cut-up noodles from the counter and enough flour to thicken the broth.

Another disagreement

Grams had to dry the noodles on the countertop all the way through for hours before cooking them in the broth. I never had the time to let them dry. I take them right from the cutting stage into the boiling broth with the same results. "How the cook makes them is how the cook makes them" was my motto. The noodles freeze well for future use, but in that case, they MUST be dried all the way through, or you will have one frozen lump to add to your boiling broth.

This recipe can be made into soup (cut the noodle

recipe in half or double the broth. Use store-bought broth if more is needed). If you leave it as is, it will make a hearty dish. It can be served with mashed potatoes to stretch the meal as the broth makes its own gravy with all that flour.

Grams was a talented and wise lady. She taught me with wisdom and patience the skills she thought a woman would need to keep a pleasant home. Plus, she taught me to quilt, embroider, sew, garden, can our vegetables, and even asked my aunt to teach me to knit. She passed away last August (1998). I inherited her recipes, her rolling pin, her gardening knowledge, and the only remaining quilt tops in the family.

Summer 1998 This really is how she taught us.

ONE GOOD DAY

AS IS MY TRADITION, A MESSAGE FOR CHRISTMAS

*H*ere you will find my annual Christmas message. For my new friends whom I have had the wonderful opportunity to make this year, you are not aware of this, but it is my tradition to write a story or message for my friends and family each year in lieu of a Christmas card.

For many have said, "After the loss of a loved one, they wished for one more day." I pondered this statement many times over the last year, knowing that death is not the only way to lose someone dear.

Exactly how would I react if all the pain was suddenly gone, and I was given one more day with that special one? Would I spend it in endless chatter with helpless giggles over past stories while holding those calloused hands? Would I rub the tired muscles or run my fingers through the always tangled mop of hair?

One more day, one more night to spend in whatever

manner we chose? To count all the stars in the night sky, watch the clouds roll by, spy on the wild animals in the park, run–really run through the fields, dance, twirl, hug, or caress.

Would I beg forgiveness for all the anger passed between, uncover the hidden hurt, toss away the misunderstandings, find a smile, and rediscover laugher?

Why, I question myself, do we ask for one more day? Or one good day only after we lose that person so dear to us? Why don't we find that good day now while we still have the time? It is because we believe those good days will never end.

Even one of the most mundane or painful of days surely has a touch of happiness in it and is better than being without. Isn't it possible to try for one better day while they are still available?

I believe we each have the ability to stretch our arms skyward, accept the energy from the universe to help us, and have that good day… today. As my Tom always used to say, "All days are good—some are just a little better than others."

This is my Christmas message. Try to find those good days.

Christmas 2004

QUILT SURPRISE

*A*t last, I completed the stitches in the series of retro-era children's quilt blocks. I embroidered these charming scenes, originally from a pattern used for decorating 1950 era tea towels, each one depicting a common household chore being attempted by a toddler.

I took the whole quilt top, batting, and backing piece of fabric to my grandparent's house for their advice on how to finish it. I had decided against hand quilting it myself since I did not have an eternity to finish a project of this size. Hopefully, the three of us would come up with an easier and less time-consuming plan.

Grams was an accomplished needleworker and quilter from the days when sewing was done by hand and not on a machine. I didn't hold out much hope of any ideas for a quick fix, but rather more of a lesson on patience and time management.

My grandfather enjoyed nosing about watching the

women work. *I wondered how long it would be before he would put his two cents worth in on this project.*

After laying out the bedcover, the imps came alive performing their chores across the quilt top. Stories flowed from the two grandparents remembering how different blocks reminded them of a special friend, a lambing time in the old wooden barn, cornstalks rustling silks out in the field, and laundry flapping on the line.

We eventually decided on a tied-style comforter as the solution to finishing the quilt. Each 'tie' floss was twisted into a French knot worked carefully into the design. We vetoed the old-fashioned overhand knot tied with pieces of yarn at symmetrically marked-off locations on the quilt top. My grandmother and I tied knots on daisy flowers with yellow embroidery floss, the leaves with green, streaks of sunshine with orange, and pink for the bunny noses. This method did not detract from the actual embroidery work in the quilt. We each had a small embroidery hoop to use if the fabric needed more tautness where wrinkles might otherwise sneak in.

Gramps had hit upon the idea of using floss to tie the knots into the existing embroidery stitches. Strategically located, the mini twirls enhanced the embroidery but not be so noticeable as a "tied" quilt would be. *He had proven to be quite helpful, after all.*

Rolling up the project, I left it there. I would return another day for more visiting and storytelling along with our version of a quilting bee.

A week went by, and the telephone rang four times

before I could run the obstacle course to answer it. Grams asked us to lunch as they needed a "baby" fix.

We were familiar with these requests as my son, the first great grandbaby in the family, joined the society of pampered grandchildren.

The air carried a hint of mystery as we arrived. The two grandparents tried to hide their sideways glances and quirky smiles during playtime. We chased each other around the large great room until the smell of hamburgers and French fries called to us from the kitchen.

I was eager to work on the quilt. They both were more interested in playtime with the toddler, which struck me as strange since they had been so eager for me to help on the project only days ago. Maybe their enthusiasm had waned. This would not be a problem. I could finish it up at home. Enjoying family time was more important.

We finished the last sip of iced tea and wiped the ketchup smears from the wiggly boy's face. Gramps finally pulled himself from his chair and decided it was time to work on the quilt. My grandmother wouldn't look at me, pretending to clean up the dirty dishes. Both looked so guilty, I had a feeling something was wrong.

We positioned ourselves around the bed. My squirmy son, with his uncanny ability to know something fun was about to happen, fell into a fit of giggles. He plopped himself in the middle of the bed. In our house, we played tent on our big bed. So, to him, this time would be no different.

I gasped as the chuckling man pulled the bundle from the closet and unrolled the quilt. There lay the beautiful project, every stitch completed. Once I was over my shock, we played 'tent,' flinging the quilt high in the air, and letting it flop back down on the happy child.

My grandmother spilled the story. To my amazement, Gramps had finished it. All the French knots? Gramps? The secret was out. My great-grandmother taught him embroidery stitches during his junior years. She did not believe in idle hands. His memory still held those lessons, and he wanted to finish the project himself. My grandmother added the binding afterward. I was so dumbfounded, words failed me.

We had the use of that quilt for only a short time. He never knew of my heartbreak when later someone stole my surprise quilt.

"See ya later, Mom. Don't worry, Suzie's not in the cookie jar," Brian hollered as he watched as she stuffed her pink hoodie pouch full of cookies. "I am taking her for a walk." They slammed out the back door. It was more like chasing Suzie than going for a walk.

"Noooo, don't do it. Suzie. Come back here!" Brian yelled as he ran at top speed after her. Suzie found the mud puddle. She jumped right in its center, spraying big glops of mud over Brian's clean clothes and the new white sports car belonging to the next-door neighbor Brian had named Mr. Big Man.

Oh, no, not again. I'm in TERRIBLE trouble.

Mr. Big Man stormed out of his front door, shaking his fat fist at them. The sparrows flew off the tree branches of the aging oak tree in his front yard while the neighborhood calico cat clawed her way up the backside of the same tree.

"I will clean up your car," Brian said. "She was only playing. She didn't mean to make a mess."

"You better believe you'll clean it up! I want to see you washing that car till it sparkles. I'll be watching you every minute."

By this time, Suzie felt it was her duty to help the scared cat. Or maybe she was only being her mischievous self. Either way, she hopped and skipped to the tree, then jumped to the lowest branch to help rescue the cat.

Although she meant well, this would only be another Suzie disaster in the making. She had tangled a foot in the tree branches. The calico cat meowed her delight at the sight of Suzie's stuck foot. Smarty Cat sat on a higher limb, swished her tail, and watched the drama beneath her unfold.

Meanwhile, Brian grabbed a fat, low limb with both hands and swung himself up the tree to help Miss Disobedient untangle her foot. The cat had nine lives; she would manage on her own.

He realized Mr. Big Man's car would have to wait until later. *Sometimes life was just not fair.* His attention would be on Suzie today.

Suzie had been Brian's best friend for as long as he could remember, but he never tamed the ornery streak out of her. Brian told his pal all his secrets and dreams. As any good friend would do, she listened quietly and offered no judgment. She loved hearing adventure stories and watching soccer and rugby on TV with Brian. Suzie mimicking the New Zealand All Blacks Rugby Team perform the Haka before their matches would send Brian into knee-slapping laughter.

Having a kangaroo for a best friend presented challenges. She had a mind of her own and, to his dismay, frequently his disobedient kangaroo's adventures ended with Brian in hot water, making apologies, or attempting to fix damages. A lot.

Plus, she was close to six feet tall and could hop at 25 miles an hour, which made it difficult to control her or for the giant fuzzball to play games with his friends. On the other hand, her high jumping made an entertaining cheering section for Brian's games. She hopped after the balls if the team needed her to fetch one which may have gone too far afield. His friends loved Suzie, though. Her fuzzy, grey, innocent face gave them fits of giggles every time they saw her.

The unusual duo traveled their familiar path to the park on Saturday, which also happened to be Farmer's Market Day. Brian schemed out a plan to take the hidden moss-covered path through the hardwood trees and away from the people who clogged the market. The apple tower cart in the center of the vendors' booths fascinated his nosy pal. It was in Brian's best interest to distract Suzie from any wild ideas which may flit through her mind.

At that very moment when Brian stepped onto the

footpath, from the sidewalk down the block, Mr. Straw Hat waved his arms over his head like a basketball player signaling his teammate on the court. He wore his usual sweat-rimmed straw hat and farmer bib coveralls, and he beckoned to them to walk in his direction.

Oh, no, ignoring Mr. Straw Hat wouldn't work. From what Brian saw, it looked like the farmer was selling the sweet corn his mom favored. He couldn't be rude. Much to Brian's better judgment, Suzie hopped, and Brian jogged over to the Farmer's Market.

"You be careful, and do not touch one single thing," Brian warned Suzie as he retrieved a bag of corn from the farmer and prepared to resume their plans for the day.

No. No. No!

Suzie spied the apple tower and headed in that direction. Her short arm took one garnet red apple from the pile. *Nothing happened.*

Nothing happened?

Until Suzie tripped over The Flower Lady's shopping bag, and her three-foot-long tail jiggled the table leg. One by one, green, red, and yellow apples began rolling down the tilting table.

"Suzie, come back here!" Brian yelled as his kangaroo sped away, making a beeline through the aisles of vendor's tables and the market grounds toward the safe green patch of lawn.

Brian juggled falling apples yet failed to save the avalanche. One by one, the fruit bounced to the ground, rolled to the feet of the customers, and became a heap of bruised, ugly apple faces.

"I apologize, so sorry. It really was an accident. She doesn't realize how big she is. Kangaroos can be rather clumsy. So sorry," the embarrassed young man continued to repeat as he stacked apple after colored apple in his arms.

Apple Man chuckled, feeling sympathy for the young juggler. "It's okay, Brian. Everyone has a bad day. No harm done. We'll be able to use the bumped ones for apple butter or applesauce. Don't worry." He offered a large bag for the bruised apples.

When Brian found Suzie, he only glared and muttered, "Let's go home."

On the way back, Brian counted to one hundred before he calmed down. Then he told Suzie about the vacation they soon would take to visit Grandma in Montana. They would ride on an airplane, and they each would have their own seat. Suzie might have a bit of trouble with her big tail, but Brian felt sure there were kangaroo seats on an airplane.

Grandma would take them to see Yellowstone National Park. Buffalo and grizzly bears lived there with animals called elk, whatever they were. He cautioned Suzie that she would need to pay extra attention to him in this park. This was not the type of park where they would be able to run and play. It would be great fun to hike on the trails, see the Old Faithful Geyser, and climb to see the waterfalls in the Canyon area.

After the trip through the market, washing Mr. Big Man's car, and playing catch with his friends; the streetlights flickered on. A neighborhood signal which all the children knew meant the end of playtime and go home.

Brian ate his favorite pot roast dinner, and the hungry kangaroo went outside to eat her moss and tree leaves. She topped it off with a dessert of flowers from the acres of the meadow behind Brian's backyard. They watched TV that evening, and before too many hours passed, the tired pair called it a night, and hustled off to bed.

"BRIAN, BRIAN, TIME TO WAKE UP. I LAID YOUR clothes out on the bed. Hurry up!" Mom yelled down the hallway. "We don't want to be late today of all days."

Brian opened his sleepy morning eyes and wondered what adventure he and Suzie would have today. He yanked his good luck, green-striped polo shirt over his head, and pulled on his favorite jeans. He ran his hands through his pillow hair, trying to finger comb out the blond spikes.

He groaned as he stretched his arms out to drag the empty wheelchair to his bedside. He pulled himself off the bed and plopped onto his ever-present mobile transportation.

Brian tugged his stuffed kangaroo out from under

the blankets and tucked her in beside his limp legs. Suzie had always been his best "mate" and traveling companion. They both rolled down the hallway to start the day.

He and his mom hoped that his visit to the doctor would be a happy one. "Maybe today will be the day our dreams finally come true, Suzie. The doctor might have good news for us."

EVEN THOUGH THIS IS A FICTIONAL STORY, I HAVE continually followed my tradition of adding detailed touches from my life to my stories. *The first line of this story is a famous one in our family. My son, Andy, would say, "I am not in the cookie jar, Mom," whenever I would ask him what he was doing. He also had a passing acquaintance with an Australian who actually owned a kangaroo named Suzie.

March 2018

THE FAITHFUL FRIEND

*H*appy thoughts and memories have swirled around me like a crown. Laughter and smiles have filled my heart. Rose petals have adorned me, and a flower basket has hung on the crook of my elbow.

Tears have been shed down my front with a sadness rising from such depths, even my own heart has felt like it would crack. My straight back was there to hold up the friends who sat with me as they asked for help in their healing.

Those weak in health have used me for support when their legs would no longer hold them. Some who were short on breath found their way slowly to my loving arms by sheer will. My sturdy strength was always available to hold them up.

Babies and children have slept and cuddled in my lap. Where there should have been silence, a slight snore or giggle often erupted from precious mouths. As they grew, these twigs of children have hopped and climbed on me, often leaving inch long scratches or small bruises scarring my body with their hard-toed shoes while uncaring others looked on.

Vibrations of a joyous noise often rocked my feet and tapped into the roots of my ancestors while wonderful music whirled about. Choir voices lifted my spirits like branches reaching skyward.

Feeling the woven cloth of important dignitaries as they nestled next to me during great ceremonies had given me opportunities to think of the diversity, history, traditions, and stories of many cultures. Their kind words of wisdom convinced me of a wonderful world to come.

Throughout my life, yes, there have been those my strength could not reach. They looked away after seeing my scars and imperfections and were determined to cast me aside like no more than a piece of useless furniture. To me these wounds are illustrations of the experiences of my life and examples of how the spirit of loving kindness had not been fulfilled.

Belonging to a fine finishing school or sitting in a grand cathedral may not have been part of my past or my style. My value has been in my plainness.

But one day from my humble roots came an honor beyond which any growing sapling would never have expected to achieve. Friends now come to visit me as I sit in the museum of great men. I am their faithful friend, an old country church pew.

2018 written for a pastor friend

The inspiration for this story was President Jimmy Carter who lives and worships at Maranatha Baptist Church in Plains, Georgia. He sits in an aisle pew in what I would believe by now would be a well-worn seat. It was my goal to personify the life of the old wooden church pew on which our President may still now sit. (2020)

THE FORGOTTEN CHRISTMAS BEAR

"Oh, no! How did I forget Heidi's Christmas Bear? What was I thinking, or not thinking as the case may have been?" I said to myself as I bounced off one wall to another. No, I wasn't drunk, but I was having a bit of vertigo from an inner ear problem.

I scurried to the calendar. *If I ran to the store… wait, Toys "R" Us closed this year. Where would I find the "right bear?"* Finding the "right" bear is not the easiest of tasks. There are enormous bears, baby bears, happy bears, grumpy bears, soft bears, and stiff bears. How would I have time to find the "Christmas Bear," wrap it, and fight the long line at the "pretend" Santa Helper express service…. (disguised as the post office) with its merry elf helpers and HOPE it would arrive in time for Christmas? *Do this while my head was in a whirling, twirling universe. Oh, sure!*

Backstory

"Heidi, put that bear back where you found it," said Judy, her mom, as she and I visited during a slow time in my floral shop.

"Judy, if it is okay with you, I would like her to have it," I said. "Heidi usually picks out flowers from the cooler, but if she would rather have the bear, I would 'gift' it to her instead. She never asks for much."

"Okay, if you are sure."

Therein started a tradition. Heidi had picked the floppiest, softest, stretched out flat on her tummy, brown bear to take home. From that day forward, although I had moved out of state, Heidi received a bear from me every Christmas.

The year or two when her mother protested "No more bears, her bed and room look like a zoo!"

I replied with, "When there are too many, donate them to Toys for Tots!"

I pulled back for a Christmas or two and sent her a bear-themed lap quilt I had made or a piece of pretty jewelry. She loved to show her "bling" off at her alternative learning environment.

I was sure Judy would have forgotten her protests after I threw her off guard with the jewelry, and the next year I would send another bear. One year, a bear as large as Heidi went via elf express. It was a big hit with her fellow classmates, as well. I imagined her toting that fur ball around all day. That year, I received a picture of her with that bear. I laughed, and I cried.

WHAT TO DO? WHAT TO DO? IT WAS THE ELEVENTH HOUR. How completely dumb could I be? Well, extremely dumb if one really wanted to know! My head was still whirling with a severe case of vertigo, but I was determined to finish this task.

The internet to the rescue! I scrolled, typed, hunted, and no bear was the right bear to suit my exacting standards.

What would a young lady like? No more jewelry. I was bored with sending that gift. But, aha, Bath and Body Works for girly, smelly stuff! YAY! I may be dizzy, but my brain still functioned. *Well, semi-functioned.* I ordered her a gift card, (with an assurance from the company that it would arrive before Christmas Day). This way she could pick out her own goodies (remember the original shopping trip in my florist? Heidi knew what she liked) with Mom's help, of course. Most of the time, I think the internet is a pain but not today.

She will have a present only not a bear this year.

At this point, I will add, Heidi will be 43 in January, a special needs young lady whom I love dearly. This past year she was diagnosed with stage IV liver cancer and no reasonable medical treatments were available to her. Next year, I am hoping and praying, she will be here to have another Christmas Bear.

Christmas 2018

Sadly, she did not see Christmas 2019. She passed away in the summer of 2019.

Heidi's mom told me this winter, 2020, that Heidi's young cousin was given permission to pick any bear she would like from the zoo in Heidi's room. She chose the giant bear, and it now has a forever home with someone to cuddle it at night, just as Heidi did.

THE GERMAN BOYFRIEND

I loved the daily walks with my roommate. She and I had been friends for three years. We were new to the apartment complex and had enjoyed meeting the characters who were our neighbors.

I stared as the two guys across the parking lot exited their doorway and began walking our way. The uniforms gave them away.

Wow, police officers. I heard Kelly chuckling and saw her shaking her head as she stood next to me. She knew me so well.

The first officer stepped forward, and he and Kelli exchanged introductions. They shook hands while I inched farther behind my friend. Normally not shy around others, these two guys were a bit intimidating. The first guy identified himself as Jamie, and his companion's name was Duke.

Jamie said, "He thinks he is John Wayne. But he

really has a German name no one can pronounce, so it was easier to call him The Duke. He is a man of few words, and he is certainly not a morning guy," Jamie said.

Duke offered a greeting that resembled more of a low growl than a hello. I nearly whimpered as he towered over me. I wondered if he had an aristocrat's background. He had such a regal bearing.

As days passed, I watched Duke from our second-floor balcony. Every day he played ball with Jamie, which gave me an excuse to watch them. Jamie couldn't throw him one that would fool Duke. He caught the fastball, curveball, or grounder every time. He certainly was an athletic hunk.

"Face it, girl, you have a major crush on that guy," Kelli said. "I don't think you are sitting out there only admiring my garden."

Admiring is right. It wasn't the garden that caught my attention.

One balmy Friday evening, Kelli decided we should stop in for a friendly visit with our neighbors. Either she wanted to visit Jamie, or she wanted me to develop the mad crush I had on Duke into something more serious. Either way, much to my dismay and case of nerves, off we went.

Duke situated himself on the farthest end of the couch. I could feel his stare as if we were intruding on his space. I sat primly on a chair close to him. There was no reason to be nervous. The brute never uttered a syllable the whole time we were there.

Well, that certainly was a waste of time.

Saturday morning Kelli and I were out for our routine run around the block. As we turned the corner, there were Jamie and Duke jogging on the sidewalk, and neither one was panting or breaking a sweat. We didn't interrupt their run, but after looking at those muscles, I felt my heart beat faster.

He had the complete package, impressive looks, long flowing hair, and an athletic body. His personality could use a little work, but I guess one can't have everything. *That would be one long work in progress.*

I was so distracted watching Duke run; I walked right into the street as an oncoming car was heading right at me. A streak of dark hair blazed over me. Duke reached down, flipped me onto his shoulder, and then he dropped me onto the ground, out of the path of the car. He shook his head at me to show his disgust at my lack of brains. Once Jamie and Kelli knew I was not hurt, they doubled over in laughter at the sight of my flopped body on the grass.

From that day forward, when Jamie and Duke went to play ball or for their run, I made myself scarce. *No more balcony gazing.* Finally, one morning Kelli called Jamie to wait a moment and asked if we could walk with them. It had become apparent to her that since my less than elegant rescue, Duke continued to glance up at our balcony as they went by. I had not been aware of this.

So down the stairs, we went to walk with the guys. Duke courteously took my leash in his mouth. Apparently, he would be in control now, and my safety would be guaranteed.

My heartthrob was escorting me around the block. *I guess he noticed me after all.* What petite Yorkie could ever feel afraid with a gigantic German Shepherd boyfriend as her bodyguard?

Side note: Yes, my mini-Yorkie, Zoe, had a major crush on the neighbor's baseball-catching German Shepherd. That part is true. Kelli was my neighbor. Duke did not save Zoe from a speeding car. That part is make-believe.

Normal, Illinois Summer 2014

THE LADY IN PINK

*H*opping on a bus to travel halfway across the country for my fiftieth birthday visit was not one in which I expected anything other than boredom. *How wrong could I have been?*

What characters I saw on my bus and in the terminals! I sat with the most wonderful Black man who kept me laughing for many miles. He chuckled at the antics of a young Black teen-aged girl sprawled on the seats in front of us. Each time a new passenger would load, she would pull her head under a blanket imitating a turtle, pretending to be asleep so she wouldn't have to share her seat. Her head popped out from under the blanket shell when she heard his safety call. The gentleman would call out, "That's my girl," when all was clear. They weren't related; he was only helping her in this friendly, kind manner and providing us all with a merry laugh.

After we stopped, and I transferred to a new bus, there was a man who appeared to be all arms and legs and would pass for the tallest human I had ever seen. He had sprawled himself across two seats (one being the last empty seat on the bus). The brat only relinquished his seat to me when I grumbled to the bus driver. An argument ensued between Mr. Spider Legs and the driver. The driver then saw no problem in evicting "Legs" for having no ticket. Then, I had two seats all to myself. Thank you, sir, for being so obnoxious.

For our musical enjoyment, the petite Mexican lady who traveled with two identical infants crooned to them a Spanish lullaby in a lovely, soft voice. She sat in the rear of the bus on a lounge-style seat where her babies lay. Her soothing voice floated forward, mesmerizing her busload audience. I could imagine the light strumming of a classical guitar accompanying her in other circumstances, possibly on a moonlit beach with waves lapping on the shore.

Later, we knew the sweet notes from the back seat would come to a halt as the groans from the other passengers echoed down the aisles like falling dominoes as we watched a rock band boarding.

Not only did they have a rock band image of long hair, tattoos, and earrings, but it was evident that they were a rock band. (Well, honestly, I am not psychic; I saw the guitars being loaded. I had hoped they wouldn't do a practice rehearsal on the bus.)

I would never have guessed what happened at pick-up points when passengers hopped off the bus, ran to the McDonalds, and did not return at the specific time as instructed by the driver. I guess I figured the bus driver was a kindly old gent and would wait. Wrong. He had a schedule to keep, closed the doors, and off we rolled.

"See ya later," we shouted and waived to the musicians standing with mouths agape and Big Macs in hand.

One of the most unusual sights on this journey was the lady-in-pink. After re-boarding at one of the many bus terminal stops, where we could take the time to stretch our legs, I repositioned myself behind the driver. All my traveling companions had reached their destination, and I was once again on my own.

No one appeared to pay this lady any mind as she sat upon two parcels waiting for her bus. With downcast eyes and no smile, she looked so forlorn. I felt a sense of loneliness creep into my bones like that of missing a friend.

Well known for my inquisitive nature and never-ending questions, my curiosity overcame my manners, and I inquired of the bus driver whether he might know about this lonesome soul? There was no rhyme or reason why I thought the man would know. I had a hunch and followed it. In fact, the driver did know about her, and he told me her story.

The point of the tale appeared that the lady-in pink was, in fact, homeless. She traveled by bus from one station to another. It was always warm in the stations.

Caring people who recognized her helped by buying her meals plus adding a few spare dollars to her pocket. She did not cause a fuss, and when in need of extra money, she took to the streets to panhandle.

The odd part of the story was that she did not stay at "home" on the street, as one would imagine. She wasn't the stereotypical homeless person. Once she had enough money for a ticket, she would board a bus and travel to another town. No one knew where she had lived, or if she had a family. She apparently didn't wish to divulge her life's secrets. She traveled across the country by bus and always wore pink was all anyone knew of her.

I rode and pondered this for many miles. That was what I called one of those "missed opportunities." I could have left the bus to visit with her but did not. I, therefore, missed a chance to acquaint myself with another "character" who may have enriched my life. Of more importance, I missed an opportunity to offer a bit of help to one so badly in need. I often wished life's lessons didn't arrive so far after the fact.

The rest of my journey was filled with more unusual characters, but none so profoundly etched in my mind as the lady-in-pink.

The year 2000, a trip from Colorado to Illinois.

THE LITTLE LAMB

*I*t was a big sky morning in Montana when the door to the florist slowly opened and in walked a middle-aged woman. Before I could offer a greeting, she burst into tears. Right in front of my eyes, I was witnessing this woman have a total loss of composure.

Grabbing the tissues, I ran around the counter, led her to a nearby chair, and held her hand with a feeble effort to offer her comfort.

Once her emotions were under control, she was able to choke out the words that her ten-day-old grand-daughter had passed away. She had come to ask me to design the flowers for the baby's funeral.

"Oh, my," were not the most brilliant words that had ever left my mouth, but at this moment were the only words I could muster. *A baby.* I reached for the tissues once again, this time for myself.

After assuring her it would honor me to assist the family and attend to the details of her request, I walked her to the door of her car, returned to the shop, and promptly locked the door. *I needed time to meditate over this and decide upon a design. A baby, oh my.*

To me, designing flowers is a passion that I embraced with much joy. To design flowers for any funeral requires me to see beyond stems and petals. I needed to envision the person and the life to be honored, and in this case, also the family. Strength, compassion, and love were what I needed this day and the ability to portray these with flowers.

Well into the evening I worked, placing each delicate pink and white flower in the exact location as if each flower had a message to tell this little baby girl. A message that they loved her, even if for the shortest time. That was my thought anyway.

Before delivery the following morning, I added a small cuddly baby lamb to the center of the piece.

With a heavy heart for the family, I entered the funeral home to place my flowers on her tiny casket. As I approached her forever bed with flowers in my arms, I halted as if riveted to the floor. In front of me was that tiny doll-like child with a baby lamb in her arms. *A lamb.*

A week later, a young lady entered my shop. This young lady let her heavy, swollen eyes move from the floor to meet mine. I watched the tears roll slowly down her cheeks.

Oh no, not again. Not another one.

"How could you possibly have known?" were the only words she haltingly asked of me.

"I just knew," I told her as I held this perfect stranger in my arms. "I just knew."

This is a true story, one of many similar
instances in my life in which "I just knew."

Christmas 2004

THE MYSTERY OF WHERE ONE WILL
FIND GOODNESS

*M*onday morning was no different than any other morning in the chain link jungle. Each of the "locals" jockeyed for their position against the fence surrounding the park, all the while keeping a wary eye on their meager possessions. The tiny man looking for all the world like a leprechaun as he spread open his newspaper and continued reading nonstop from front to back absorbing the printed word. He was seemingly oblivious to all those around him. Peripheral vision and acute hearing must have blessed the man as he could describe in detail the gait, accent, and fashions of those who hustled by.

Once the morning reading was over, he would idly chat with those around him. He would open his battered case, pull out a worn guitar, and begin the ritual of strumming a tune. On the rare occasion when a child would pass by, the scholar-musician would pull out a balloon and fashion an animal from its snake-like length. He smiled and one could almost see his heart swell at the joy a child would express at his gift. It became obvious from the stories told by those around him that he had seen way too much hurt and pain in the world and was determined to use his time on earth to bring happiness to others.

Some of his recent happy times were talking with a newcomer to the daily crowd. This young lady could not be more than eighteen or so, but she conducted herself with much more maturity and confidence than one would expect from someone her age. She was spending her summer in the big city studying at the university. She never failed to wish him good times on her way to class and always brought him a bite to eat on the trip back. He suspected she went without lunch on many occasions. Grateful for her kindness, he would tell a joke or sing a song to her. He always promised to grant her one wish. She rewarded him with a dazzling smile and a head tilt which undoubtedly was her "signature move."

As summer drew to a close, one day the little man watched his friend carry a hefty box through the park. She would stop from time to time to lighten her load. Finally, slipping through a hole in the fence, she made her way to his spot. *Why was this?* She had been distributing food from her dorm cafeteria and was not about to forget him.

And here she came back…. toting another parcel.

By the determined set of her mouth and the now familiar head tilt, he knew she meant business. She explained it was time for her departure as classes ad ended and there was no room to pack this item. The man's facial expression could only be described as incredulous as he realized this was her quilt from home. This young miss had given of herself for his comfort. Tears formed streaks down his dusty face as he tipped his emerald-green replica of a leprechaun's hat to her. She waved and walked away as he wished her good luck.

Did he wonder to himself as he stroked the quilt, "What magic had brought this young person into his life? What prompted her to give him her quilt?"

And did the young girl wonder to herself on her trip home, "Did the man have magic in that leprechaun's personality…and the hat…she had never seen it before…could he possibly be…?" One never knows . . . She never did give him her wish.

Christmas 2003

Jennifer (my daughter) in fact did make a trip alone to New York City to attend summer college for six weeks when she was eighteen and did meet and feed many of the homeless there.

There really is this magical leprechaun man in Bozeman, Montana where Jennifer also lived, worked, and continued her same giving ways.

THE NAME STORE

*N*icholas sat on the crooked, splintered, wooden bench on the corner of the old town square with Mr. Toby. Mr. Toby had deep lines that wrinkled his face around his eyes. His skin resembled the color of black walnut hulls. The elderly man sat hunched over his cane for balance as he rested on the bench.

The youngster attended the grade school three blocks from the town square. He liked to visit with his elderly friend after school. They talked about lots of fun things, like how long it took to make a ball out of bits of aluminum foil, the number of inches in a kite string, or how dogs can smell their buried bones in the dirt. Mr. Toby was so smart. He knew just about everything.

The boy had golden blond hair and twinkling ice-blue eyes. In later years girls would be holding back an old-fashioned swoon.

Nicholas, the neighborhood human energizer bunny, had latched onto Mr. Toby. His imagination was full of his make-believe adventure tales that he willingly told to anyone who would listen. He hopped up and down and enthusiastically acted out scenes when he arrived at the good parts of his stories. Today, Nicholas told Mr. Toby his mom was going to have his baby sister soon.

Mr. Toby said, "What will her name be?"

"I don't know."

"You mean your mom and dad haven't bought it yet?" Mr. Toby asked with a sparkle in his eyes.

Nicholas shrugged and appeared puzzled at such an unusual question.

"You have a pleasant name, Nicholas. Where did they buy your name?"

"I don't know, Mr. Toby. Where do you shop for names?"

"Well, at the Name Store, of course."

"Where is the Name Store here in our town?" asked Nicholas.

"I'm not sure. It has been some time since I had to shop for one. I guess you'll have to search for it, Nicholas. It would be quite an adventure."

"There are lots of stores here. I'm sure I will find it. I will search for a name for my baby sister and see how much it will cost." Nicholas scooted down off the bench.

Mr. Toby giggled as he watched his young friend run down the sidewalk and skid to a stop at the first store he saw. He tugged the door open. The chime announced his presence, and Nicholas bounded in. No explorer had more enthusiasm than this young scout.

He stopped at one of his favorite stores. "Mr. Sweet, do you know where I can find the Name Store? I want to buy a name for my baby sister," Nicholas asked as he eagerly approached the owner of Mr. Sweet's Candies.

"Nicholas, we don't have names here. We only sell candy," said Mr. Sweet. "I have lollipops and chocolate bars. I am sure she will like those."

"Ok, thank you, but not right now. She isn't even born yet," he said, flapping his arms. "I need to find her a name. Bye for now." Nicholas swung open the door and ran back outside, scanning the sidewalk in both directions in case he overlooked a shop in his haste to see Mr. Sweet.

There were several ladies with children coming out of the store next door, so surely Mr. Tinker would know.

"Mr. Tinker, with all these toys in your shop, do you have names to sell?" Nicholas explained the reason for his shopping trip.

"Oh, my, Nicholas, I only have toys today," Mr. Tinker said with a mischievous chuckle. "Bell would be nice or Dolly, though if you want to name her after a toy."

"That will never do, Mr. Tinker. She is a baby, not a toy!"

Nicholas ran into the jewelers with all the sparkly bracelets and rings in the window.

No luck, what kind of name is Ruby or Sapphire for a baby? What is wrong with these people?

He saw sandals, ladies' shoes, and baby shoes in the next window as he peeped over the sill. To his dismay, he felt there would be no baby names here. He should have known better.

The florist lady had flowers with girl's names like Lily, Rose, Fern, and Daisy, but no names to sell.

This was becoming quite a chore. *How did people name their babies if they couldn't find the right store?*

Nicholas even tried the door that had the words 'baby gifts' printed on it. Surely, here there would be names for babies. They had a sale on cribs, which was nice. Stacked around the store, he saw diapers, blankets, and bottles but no shelves or bins with names. *This was ridiculous.* The ladies in the store all said he was such a wonderful brother to help find a name for his sister, even though they placed their hands over their mouths after they praised him. *Maybe they weren't grandma's age, but they sure acted as weird as she often did.*

After visiting every store on the town square, Nicholas' head hung low, and his shoulders slumped. He decided it was time to go home. *What sort of town could this be with no Name Store?* With his hands in his pockets, he kicked up dust puffs and rocks on his way back through the park. He spied Mr. Toby sitting on their favorite bench talking to his mom.

"There you are," she said. "I've been looking for you. Where have you been?"

"I've been looking for The Name Store, so I could help find a name for my baby sister. I couldn't find it," sighed Nicholas.

His mom's eyes opened wide like they did when a bug bit her. Her mouth made a big O.

Mr. Toby laughed and told his mother the story from the beginning.

She then explained, "Nicholas, Mr. Toby was teasing you. Dad, you, and I will sit down together and decide on a name we all like for your baby sister. We will do it as a family, so she knows how much we loved doing that for her."

"You will tell me all about your adventure and I'll write it in her baby book. We'll do a wonderful make-believe story, tell her how you fought many battles to find her a name, and then add the proper story, too. You may act out the scenes every year when we celebrate her birthday. It will be the start of a family tradition."

Nicholas beamed an enormous smile. Nicholas then gave Mr. Toby a big hug and thanked him for helping to start a new custom in his family. Mr. Toby sure was smart.

Winter 2018

THE NEW GUY

$\mathcal{T}$he new guy strode down the hallway gazing languidly from side to side at the grade school students who stared at him. The girls giggled behind their hands at how handsome he was with his ginger colored, wavy hair, and soft brown eyes. The boys scoffed at his vest and orange neck scarf. What kind of name was Zander they had all snickered? As hard as it was for a newcomer to adjust to a new school, his self-assurance appeared to make him immune to any negatives which came his way. Apparently being different and jeered at were incidents he was accustomed to, or at least he hadn't realized he was different.

His teachers commented on his quiet attitude, and how he was always willing to speak when asked. His voice and accent were a little gruff but otherwise easily understood. His manners were impeccable, shaking hands as he met adults and students alike. He played ball like a pro and always included the special needs students who were hesitant to join.

One day he even pulled a tiny kindergarten student from under a falling bucket that had been forgotten on a ladder in the hallway. He was known to nudge his way in between a swaggering class bully and his trembling victim. This would tactfully let the bully know his actions were not acceptable in Zander's world.

This year the school began a new project, a green garden which would help the children understand how to grow vegetables. Volunteers arrived to help the students till the soil and plant the seeds. Zander understood this process well. Living on a farm had given him experience in digging and planting. Gardening was no different than playing in the dirt.

He wiggled his way right through the middle of the group and into the dirt patch. Shortly, he was up to his elbows in the rich, dark earth making the soil fly in all directions as he dug and scooped his way down the row. Those behind him had to duck for cover!

His rows were a bit crooked as he took the time to pull up the fat earth worms and any buried treasures he found along the way. The girls screamed and the boys hooted when he found the worms. Each mini gardener began to understand the process, and within the hour the garden was planted. Zander was then pleased to lead the way to the water hose for a good soapy arm and leg scrub.

As time wore on, the principal noticed his students

acted more like a large family. Bullies were less angry and not warming the seat in his office as frequently. The shy and disadvantaged students were more focused on their abilities. They were making great strides in confidence. Many were seen whispering secrets to him. Others let him listen to their reading when they struggled. The principal felt this new fellow's aura and warmth made a change in the children. Being different didn't make a difference to anyone when Zander was around. The students wanted to be like him and be his buddy.

It was the principal's custom with all new students, to make a ninety-day call to the family to report on how the student was adjusting. After the pleasantries had passed and his assessment concluded, the principal said, "I am happy to report that Zander is doing better than we could have ever imagined. We will be pleased to have this great dog continue with the "Comfort Dog Program.""

THE QUILTER'S GIFT

*I*n the shadow of the mountains lived Lily, a diminutive lady with a natural curly mop of hair the color which rivaled that of an Irish setter. She had stunningly beautiful eyes with the gemlike quality of an emerald. Lily bubbled over with energy, and it was obvious by the firm muscles in her arms that she had not been a novice to hard farm work. Her hands revealed a few age spots coupled with the arthritic joints normally associated with people in the upper age brackets.

Making her beginning students feel at ease, she would erupt with laughter when she told stories of the funny mistakes she had made in her artistic life.

"You should have seen the time I sewed some of my squares wrong side out and didn't realize it until I completed the whole top," she crowed. "Or the time I didn't buy enough fabric of the dominant color I needed. By the time I finished that quilt with the substitute colors, only the dog loved it."

Lily would take the fumbling, unskilled hands of her students and coach their stitches into their first project. Many stitches were too large, a few stitching lines resembled a dog's crooked hind leg. Stitch by stitch, the eager group learned the age-old art of hand quilting.

"I have insisted this is the world's easiest quilt," she told her greenhorns, as she began the beginner's class. "It is a few larger beginner blocks which surround a focal panel." Miss Lily liked to keep to the western theme. She taught her classes in an old bunkhouse on the family's homestead where her staff hung other sample class quilts. She even wore western shirts to class with mother-of-pearl snaps on the pockets and boot-cut jeans.

She is either blind or deaf. She turned her back to us, as my classmates and I rip out the mistakes in our work We picked out those stitches and smiled innocently when she glanced our way. As one of us looked to the other, it was not uncommon to hear a student had heaved a sigh or rolled an eyeball. No way was this the world's easiest quilt I believed could be our collective thought.

While we bent over our work, Lily told us the history of quilting, dating back from Egyptian times to the present. Being as we were in a mountain community, she felt we would like a western tale on quilting as well. She told us a cowboy's quilted bedroll was referred to as a "soughan" and he would use it anytime he rode on overnight journeys with his horse.

"In the real-old-days," she said as we all laughed, "a bride always had thirteen quilts in her hope chest by her wedding day. And most importantly," she told us as she said to all of her classes, "a quilter should always try to share her work with a charity or needy person."

After several weeks of work on this 'easy" quilt,' we students graduated with a show and tell tea party. We all showed off our work and told who the recipient of our quilt would be. Mine was going to my college son for Christmas.

During the graduation celebration, lacy snowflakes fell. As we enjoyed viewing each other's quilts and sipping hot cider, our winter wonderland had become the scene of a full-on blizzard. As the wind whipped out of a gray sky, nearly blinding our view, we hurried out to our four-wheel-drive vehicles to be on our way.

With wipers swishing full speed, seeing the dividing lines in the highway was difficult. On the roadside ahead, under the overpass, I spied flashing caution lights and a splotch of red. As I slowed to a pace like that of the old gray mare, I saw a lady wearing a red ski jacket who waved frantically.

"What is wrong?" I yelled out the open passenger side window. I had rolled down my window, but with the forceful wind blowing, I wasn't sure if she could hear me. She motioned by cupping her ear with her hand that she could not.

'

"I have a flat tire, and the car clunks when I try to drive," she hollered at me as she approached my car window. At least I thought that is what she said. I hopped out of my Jeep to walk closer to her so we could at least hear one another. We looked at the car and sure enough, the tire was flat, and a metal rod dragged the snowy ground.

"It will be some time before help will arrive in this storm, so let's wait in my car where it is warm," I offered.

"My daughter is with me, and she is sick," she said in a mother's worried tone. Her ponytail bobbed with each hand gesture. "I was on my way to the emergency room when this happened. I am so thankful you stopped. I really need help."

I peeked inside the car and saw a flaxen-haired, blue-eyed imp. Wrapped around the tiny body was a rather threadbare black and yellow plaid blanket. Thin wrists showed through a too small denim jacket and her feet were sockless in muddy brown sneakers. Neon-green painted toenails wiggled out of the holes in her shoes. A raw pixie nose sprinkled with freckles and a forced smile appeared on chapped lips as the child peered back at me. The most frightening sight was the face flushed with fever. Clearly, this mother and daughter had seen hard times.

"What is your name, little one?" I asked her.

"My name is Grace, and I am four years old," she

proudly told me. She held up four stubby fingers painted with the same awful neon-green nail polish. "And Mommy's name is Tracy. What is your name?" she chattered on. "I am boiling hot and then I am freezing," she had added, getting to the point of how rotten she felt.

"My name is Tracy. With your shiny blonde hair and sparkly eyes, you look like a princess, and doctors like to take care of princesses. So, let's see if we can find you a good doctor, okay?" I said to her.

Without hesitation, I trudged to my car, grabbed up my quilt project, and returned to Grace. I bundled the feverish girl in the new quilt while her trembling mom watched. Whether the trembling was from the cold or fear, I did not know. All I knew was this girl was badly in need of medical attention.

Once they were safely in the car, we crawled through the whiteout conditions of the snowstorm. Tracy watched the road's edge. She gave me cues whether we were still on the pavement. I white-knuckled the steering wheel to the l exit where I knew the hospital emergency room sign would appear.

Luckily for us, it seemed to be a slow afternoon so far with no other patients visible. A gurney was rolled out for Grace, and the white-coated doctor wanted to see her immediately. His collar-length and sandy-colored hair gave him more of a surfer's look than that of a serious emergency room doctor. His calm manner won him over with Grace as he pretended that he could not find his patient. Then waggled his eyebrows and made a big "O" with his mouth when she popped out from under the sheet on her bed.

"My name is Dr. Bear," he said.

Grace giggled.

"Just like a real bear. It really is my name, and I am a friendly bear, more like a lamb than a bear," he insisted.

Grace giggled even more. Even we ladies had to smile at his charm.

He gave her a thorough examination and pronounced, "Mom, I believe we have an acute case of flu here. I would like to keep her for a couple of days to watch her progress."

Dr. Bear assigned Grace to a room with the two anxious women helicoptering at her bedside. When I was assured that Grace would soon be well and Tracy had calmed, I thought it best to be on my way. The snow had continued to fall, but my home was nearby. Tracy folded up the quilt in which I had wrapped around Grace and prepared to return it to me.

At that moment I remembered Lily's words about quilters helping others. I made up my mind, I knew I would leave the quilt for Grace. There would be more quilts to make. Maybe even ones that really were easy.

And for my son, he could have the usual socks and underwear under the Christmas tree.

Christmas 2017

The only part of this story that is true is my teacher in Bozeman (name changed to protect the innocent) and the world's easiest quilt was NOT the world's easiest quilt. The rest of the story was fiction, although the lesson on giving has always remained with me.

THE QUILTER'S SON

"*I* don't understand why my friends think because I quilt, I don't mind mending. I detest sewing in zippers and fixing seams," my mother huffed.

Luckily, I am a smart son. I know better than to give her my mending. Her friends haven't caught on yet.

Being the son of a quilter is not a simple life. Every time Mom needs a shopping companion for fabric, who does she call? *Me!* I have never known if she trusts me or if none of her friends who are in their right mind will go with her.

"You have ten minutes in and out."

If my sister happens to be caught with Mom when the fabric alarm goes off, that is exactly what she tells our fabriholic mother. Imagine this, she gets away with it! Should the truth be told, my sister is no help, anyway. Her ability to understand coordinating colors is nonexistent. She most likely believes a color wheel is a mandala or a game in a casino.

I must admit I don't always know why orange polka dots mixed with purple flowers or green stripes work well together, but I have come to realize over the years that the mind of a quilter is a bit off the grain, anyway.

The one rule I have is there should be no black in a baby quilt. Occasionally, I win. If I pick out the fabric for the quilt, I win. If I am dumb enough to leave the decision up to Mom, who knows what will happen?

One splendid example is an infant quilt she made for a musician friend of mine. "The giant quarter and eighth notes are so colorful. Son, you think if there is black in the background it is such a big deal. Bright colors are wonderful for babies to focus on. If the quilt calls for it, it goes in," Mom insisted and totally overruled me.

Now, allow me to set the scene for a trip to a quilt shop with my mother. We enter the shop as any 'normal' shoppers do, which is nothing unusual. A few glances will come our way. Apparently, we look like proper clientele by our perusal of the 'stop and stare wall' at the portal to this lint-infested world.

We mark out a territory and set about conquering our first location. Now, the "show" will begin. All that is missing is a director's megaphone and the 2nd AC person (lingo for the second assistant camera) with the filmmaker's clapboard.

"Son, go back over there, reach up, and see that bolt right above your head? That swirling brown one might work. It looks like melting chocolate. Stack it on the pile," Mom hollers across the aisles.

They filled the rows with fabrics at which I gawk and can only believe the dye factory must have had an explosion. No one in their right mind would design fabric on purpose with these patterns. Maybe there had been a clearance sale of printed fabric seconds at the factory.

"No, not that one, the other one." She waves her hands like a traffic cop to show me I needed to move over one or two steps. All she needs to do now is add a salsa dance to her waving movements and we will make money on subscriptions to 'YouTube.' Other shoppers stand about stacking selections over their arms, one atop another, pretending to be interested in matching them, yet, all the while peering over the top of the bolts of fabric to see what will happen next with this weird couple of shoppers.

"No, that blue does not look right next to that brown, find something that resembles fireworks but not real fireworks." Mom envisions weird things, expects me to read her mind, and orders me back to the racks. *Please do not let see me inside her mind!*

"Huh?"

"And a white with freckles, a red that has an orange liquid fireball flashing through it, and a smushy green like crushed up grass." She continued to rattle off a list.

"How am I supposed to remember all of that?"

147

"Oh, yes, and something with wiggles but not squiggles in any color."

"Well, what's the difference?" Mom gives me the 'hairy eyeball' look, not to be confused with an eyeball roll.

"Maybe this one will work," says a perky store employee who appears out of nowhere and whose help is not in the least bit welcomed. She hands us a fabric with the most obnoxious orange curls. She does not understand our way of shopping, is hindering our mojo, and she is also in the way. Behind the helper. I see a laser glare boring into her back from Mom.

Maybe she feels the cosmic hostility, or it could have been the loud huff coming from my mother, but either way, the clerk backs off to places where banished assistants hide until it is safe to return to the store where more sane customers are shopping.

Every time I return to the bolts of fabric, I come back with a mountain-sized load I can't see over, bumping into an unused table, and toppling the whole fabric avalanche down upon it. We spread the selection out completely, taking over this table, matching and discarding, shuffling the deck, comparing it to our pattern, and the personality of the recipient.

"What if you do this?" I offer and rearrange the deck. "We have twelve bolts here. You must pick something," I coax until eventually, her selection is complete. Sure enough, as I heave a sigh of relief and return the bolts which we discarded, she spies ANOTHER one and here we go again. I am thinking the ten-minute rule of my sisters is not such a bad idea after all.

Looking like Sherpas, we finally waddle off to the cutting table where there is the obligatory quilter's chit-chat with the clerks about our selections. I smile at all the ladies agreeing with them that yes, indeed; I am a most worthy and wonderful son.

"Will this trip never end?" I think. Finally, the sack of valuables that we carry out the door is no bigger than the bag of dog food Mom buys for her tiny Yorkie.

"All of that work for this little bag?" I begin to comment but catch myself in time as I feel the 'look' coming my way again.

In addition to these glorious outings, our home is also unique. Where normal people have pictures of lovely seaside landscapes or family portraits, our walls have flannel coverings with random pieces of fabric stuck to them.

The dining table has a sewing machine located where my dinner plate once upon the greatest of my memories held such wonderful feasts. If it is possible to find a seat where no sewing project rests, I balance my paper plate on my lap. If Mom is cooking, real China has long been banished and if a carton has partitions in the container and written directions on "how to microwave" she considers it a meal requirement fulfilled with all the food groups accounted for.

"Why would you need more than one sewing machine?" I foolishly asked her one day.

"For the same reason, you have more than one guitar," she flippantly answered.

I never broached that subject again, even when an embroidery machine was adopted into the sewing machine community.

If a drawer were once empty, it now holds gadgets, tape measures, and what would qualify as a medieval torture tool that she uses to cut fabric. I even found a seam ripper in with the forks. She even stuffed the pantry with fabric. She calls it her 'stash.' I call it 'a forced diet.' A pantry stash should be loaded with extra food.

"How many times have I stepped on pins in the carpet?" I ask myself as I hobble along after being stabbed once again. We won't have to worry about burglars in our house. The living room is booby-trapped. *"How many other quilters use the armrest of the couch as a pincushion?"* My elbows are testimony to the pinpricks of homeless needles.

I have renamed Sundays at our house as 'Sewing Sundays.' Not so long ago, they used to be 'Baking Sundays.' The whir made by the Nascar-like pedal to the metal on the sewing machine now replaced the smell of baking banana bread or chocolate chip cookies. If I want those smells to waft through the house, I do the baking myself.

Now to my way of thinking, a quilt is warm, cuddly, and wraps around all my body. But, oh no, in our home, I find quilted wall hangings, table runners, pillows, potholders, and what I call 'handkerchief quilts.' A handkerchief quilt is my term for what I understand quilters refer to as a lap quilt. We have everything but a variety of full-length-body-sized quilts.

I scoff, "A quilt is not a quilt unless it covers my entire body." No wonder we do not have many full-sized-man quilts around. She hasn't finished them! They are referred to in the quilting world as UFOs, not the alien UFO spaceships as I always believed a UFO to be since mere childhood. A UFO is an Unfinished Object in the minds of quilters. *Of course, it is how silly of me.*

Mom has a giant-size U-Haul packing box full of them. *She surely doesn't believe I will finish them, does she?* I ask myself as the pile grows. And we know my non-domestic sister will not. This is a dilemma. Why in the world would we have unfinished quilts when there are freezing children in the world, as in her own household who need these cuddly warm works of art from her very loving hands? Note the sarcasm. *Well, I must butter her up if I am ever going to receive more than one in my lifetime, should I not? I must hatch a plot to overcome her obsessive reason for NOT finishing these projects. I have yet to figure out the plot.*

Recently, I was looking for an old picture, hoping to find it in the family album. I found an album all right. Several albums, in fact, are full of pictures of her finished quilt projects.

"Great, just great. Nowhere is the one and only picture I was searching for."

I found a surprising bit of history in these portfolios of her work, though. She has a personal rule of which I was unaware. Family members including nieces and nephews, and special friends who graduate from high school, receive an Aunt Barb quilt if they are going on to college. If not, they receive one when they decide to marry. If by chance a baby is to be born because of an unfortunate lack of aforethought, the baby is the only recipient of an Aunt Barb quilt. The pictures and stories in the albums made sense. It was a book of memories of the family members and the documentation of the individual quilt. Like the one she made for the little girl who, when she was old enough, took her baby quilt to show and tell on 'Q' day. There are those people who journal or scrapbook. Mom tells our history through her quilts and the stories she pens about them.

Today, I am sitting here, waiting for the cookies to finish baking. Yes, I am doing the baking. And… I hear the familiar rustling of fabric in the "stash." *Sigh*

"I thought I had a sapphire blue in here on this shelf. It must be the sapphire blue of a perfect morning sky. These other blues will not work," she mumbles to herself.

Oh no, here it comes. I had hoped she was only talking to herself, but I know better. I think we are going to be off on another mission for the perfect piece to sew into the next UFO. I take off my grease-stained baking apron and realize the button on my shirt has fallen off.

I hesitate, chuckle, and say, "Um, oh Greatest of

Mothers, give me a minute to sew on this button." I have learned this lesson. I do my own mending. Such is the life of a quilter's son.

Christmas 2017

True story enacted frequently and to the delight or horror of the onlookers. The son does his own mending on most occasions—the daughter does not, nor does her mother do it for her.

THE SPIRIT OF ADVENTURE

*P*atty and I became friends when she transferred into my school from across the state. Patty was five feet short with a straight pixie style to her dishwater blonde hair. She bubbled over with a personality that attracted people to her like flies to honey. But it was the sapphire blue eyes that held the greatest mystery. *I sensed hidden mischief.*

She could have had anyone for a friend, but she chose me. I am two inches taller than Patty. My waist-length hair would have made a wonderful horse's tail. It was dark and thick and looked especially great in a fancy hairstyle, but on most days, I wore it straight. My eyes were enormous, almost almond-shaped with more of a hazel green cast than brown. I held my own in the curvy figure department. I had met my match in Patty. She and more introspective with me being of the lesser trustworthy personality. I watched her with owl eyes and wondered what went on in that brain of hers.

Tonight, the air was crisp, inviting thoughts of football games and crunchy apples. The sky had so many twinkling stars; it was like silver glitter had spilled over navy blue velvet. The quaking aspens waved to us as we jogged by. I imagined the Colorado blue spruce would soon be covered by winter snows. Patty wanted me to meet her new friends from a school across town. I wasn't so sure about this great idea, but her enthusiasm for life was always so contagious. I gave in to see her smile.

Her friends Dave, Jose, and Mary were from Hollywell or "Holyhell" as students from our school called it. Hollywell was our rival school. It was an inner-city school, the one the townies attended. It was a mystery bag of skin colors and backgrounds, none of which we understood. Add a switchblade, long hair, and an occasional foreign accent, and the picture was complete.

Patty and I went to the "mountain school" which was considered a school for the upper crust. Kids whose parents had money attended classes here. Students of different cultures were normally not enrolled. By no means did my family have money. We shared bedrooms and hand-me-down clothes. The only reason we lived in this area was for my dad's job. He was doing research for an environmental company. We moved here years ago, not realizing the financial divisions which existed until much later.

Patty, on the other hand, was rich. The type of wealthy people who had so many pieces of silverware at dinner, you watched everyone else to make sure you weren't making a fool of yourself by using the wrong fork. There was even a private phone booth in an alcove of their home. The pleasant thing about her was unless you knew, you couldn't tell she was beyond loaded. Much to her mother's dismay, she liked to shop at the Salvation Army, which I thought was strange. My friend thought it was way cool. She was unique and craved the unusual.

To say Dave, Jose, and Mary were friends of Patty's probably was an exaggeration. She had flirted with Dave, one of the guys she met at an away football game. He returned the flirt by inviting her to a house party after the game. That qualified him as a friend in her book.

The sun was setting over the mountain tops, and it was our intention that evening to hang out and ride the 'ones.' The three invited us to join them. Patty was hoping for a new and exciting evening since she had these new friends.

Dave appeared to be the funny man. With that curly mop of rust-colored ringlets and rumpled appearance from head to toe, he appeared to have continually slept in his clothes. He was humorous, wiggling his brows, or cracking a joke. But his eyes were never still, always moving adding a mysterious air to him. To my way of thinking, this gave him an untrustworthy vibe.

Jose was the serious one. His goal was to be an architect after college. He loved puzzles and trying to figure out how to construct any building he saw. His shirt always looked neatly pressed. Even his jeans had a crease line. He opened doors for Mary and checked to see if we were comfortable. His features would have been great on the movie screen, chiseled jutting chin, ebony eyes, sparkling white teeth, and a voice like melted chocolate. For Pete's sake, he even played the guitar.

Mary was the clingy go-along gal. Jose had her giggling every time he looked her way. It thrilled the ditzy girl to be with her guy and hang out with the group. Her intention was to become a nurse, and she already held a volunteer position at the hospital. The future was sunshine, lollipops, and unicorns for her.

We scrambled into Jose's car, a 1960 Ford Falcon station wagon as it had more room. The four-door car was white with wooden side panels and heavily coated with road dust. Threadbare upholstery told the tale of many bottoms sliding across the once sturdy fabric. A Fisher-Price farm animal bounced about on the floor. I knew at one time this must have been the family car. Now it belonged to Jose.

We passed jabs at each other about everything from school mascots to cheerleaders and hooted at every good dig. Tonight was unusual as there was no traffic. We saw no one from either school hanging out their car windows yelling or beating on car hoods while trying to outwit the cops. A bass beat from a radio blasting down the one-way street was cause for a ticket for disturbing the peace if the driver couldn't circumvent the law enforcement. We all tried it anyway. It was a challenge. This evening boredom overtook the challenge.

"We need to take these greenhorns to our secret hideaway." Dave told us of midnight hikes the three trekked to their 'special' place. Passing winks at each other, they assured us we would enjoy it.

"Come on, give us a hint." No matter how hard we coaxed, they would not give us any details. We had nothing better to do, and our curiosity outweighed our boredom, so we agreed to go. Maybe here was the adventure Patty was craving.

We drove up and around old mountain roads until Joe finally pulled to the side of an off-road path. The car doors flew open, and out we jumped. Mary swung open the tailgate door.

"Man, this is gonna be so much fun," Dave said. Dave and Jose pulled out dusty coveralls from the cargo area. After donning the soiled suits for themselves, they gave us each a pair.

"Put these on. They will keep your clothes clean and protect your arms and legs from scrapes," Mary said.

Jose retrieved two flashlights and slipped one into his pocket and handed the other to Dave.

Following the boys, we strained to pull ourselves up the side of the mountain. We grasped at the sagebrush growing from the slope to help us in the climb. Loose pieces of gravel and slate slipping out from beneath our feet made the struggle even more hazardous. This was sweaty work in those overalls and not what I had imagined being the start of an exciting adventure.

Within minutes, Jose, our leader, dropped to his knees behind tangled underbrush and disappeared. One by one, Dave and Patty did the same. Then it was our turn.

"What are these guys up to?" I elbowed Patty. We were both bewildered.

"I suggest I wait here in case of an emergency," I said. Echoed hoots of peer laughter from beyond the bushes bounced around us. We gave each other a shoulder shrug and did as they instructed us.

"Follow us," Mary said.

Patty trailed Mary, and I followed immediately behind Patty.

Dave, with a flashlight in his hand, became the caboose nudging me along from behind. More like nudging MY behind.

We crawled through a mountainside opening no larger than a manhole cover. Jose, who was our leader, gave us instructions to creep through a dark, damp, earthy, smelling tunnel.

I immediately put the skids on my forward movement. Talk about opening a Pandora's Box. Patty's curiosity had completely taken control of her mind. She moved forward mimicking a cat's curiosity. In about five seconds, she would be out of my sight.

"Patty, what is wrong with you? No one knows where we are or who we are with. We needed to retreat back to the entrance." At this point, I urged my friend to rethink the folly of following these idiots. Trust was another issue. We didn't know these kids well enough to go blindly along.

"Exactly how do you think we can do this, smarty-pants? There is no way to turn around. Besides, this is fun, we need to see what is in here," she said.

Logic had no place in the brains of the members of these foolhardy cave explorers. A prodding body directly behind me allowing no escape route, and peer pressure diminished any hopes I may have had of turning back.

I could feel the tunnel walls on my hips and shoulders. My head bumped the rocks above. Crawling on my belly and pulling myself with my arms was the only means of traveling forward. I had to fight the thought that there was a mountain above which could collapse on top of me at any moment. My clammy hands made mud from the tunnel dust. My heart became a bass guitar beat.

Close to fifteen minutes later, we stopped.

"Now you can stand up but stay as close to the wall as you can," Jose cautioned.

"Stand up?" I croaked out. *There was nothing to hold on to in order to help me up. How was I supposed to stand up? Claw at the wall?* I situated my back to the wall and pushed myself up into an upright position, ignoring protruding rocks jabbing my back.

Dave shown his flashlight beam downward, and it was then I understood the need for caution. We were on a two-foot ledge staring at an India ink black, open, nothingness. Inch by inch we side-stepped along the ledge, always with the wall to our backs.

Anxiety driven fear of heights would easily override the claustrophobia I experienced in the tunnel if I allowed my mind to wander.

This entire time Dave was cracking jokes, "Step on a crack, break your bones falling on your back." He set my nerves on fire. Occasionally, we returned to the baby crawl. A solid rock slab created a resting place at the end of the last wriggle.

With ringside seats, it was now possible to see the enormity of the cavern. I compared it to a sports arena, well a small arena. My brave hearted companions sat with legs dangling over the side. I sat away from the edge, far away.

Dave kicked pebbles over the side, and we heard the ricochet pinging off the wall. I couldn't tell how deep the cave was from the echo.

The flashlight's beams bounced on the stalactites like a sun's reflection on crystals. I finally calmed myself enough to appreciate how pretty this view actually was.

I convinced myself that it was possible to make it through this ordeal without the others realizing my terror. We made it in without a problem, we could make it out.

I still didn't trust Dave. Jose was the one with brains. Mary had no fear. After all, she was only along for the ride, and she trusted Jose with her life. They were from a rival school with a poor reputation. I didn't know them, but I had to believe we would be fine.

About that time Dave, the jokester, lost his grip on his flashlight. We heard the clang of metal on a rock falling to the other side of the world.

Silence then shouts of anger began flying from all directions as we each raised our voices.

"What the heck is wrong with you, man? Why would you do that?"

"That was not funny, Dave. Now, what are we going to do?"

"It was an accident. It slipped. I didn't do it on purpose. Geez, guys, what do you think I am, an idiot?" Dave yelled back at us.

Was he that clumsy or had he done it to be funny?

Accusations flew until Jose took control of the situation. With a calm voice, he laid out a plan for returning to the surface.

"Ok everyone let's calm down. If you all follow me at a slow pace, and we stay close to each other, we can crawl out of here. Do exactly what I tell you to do." Jose spoke with authority in an evenly controlled voice.

Would he remember the route in the dark? I wondered as the one remaining flashlight glow was weakening. And as we crawled back, the light fizzled completely out. Totally dark. One hundred percent black-out. Luckily, we had already passed the ledge.

Jose cautioned us again to listen to him. There were several offshoots to the tunnel. We would become lost if we did not remain in touching contact with one another. He assured us he knew the way out.

Our sense of feel was our only connection in this dark world. Now we had only Jose's memory to help us. We inch wormed our way back out onto the same path we had once used to enter.

"I feel like the elephants in the circus," I said. Our hands were to remain touching the toes of the person directly ahead, much like the elephants held each other's trunks in the circus. Each time Patty stopped, my head ran right into her butt. At least I knew she was still there.

"Will you stop it with the laughter, Dave?" I snapped every time he poked me in the backside. I used a diversion technique to block the clown. My mind focused on a vision of the velvet skies and glittering stars from earlier in the evening.

It was quite some time before I realized we were exiting the tunnel, and the stone prison no longer held us. I gulped the cool evening air, and I steadied myself on wobbly legs. *Could I be hearing things, what was Dave saying?*

"That was so great. I knew we would be fine with Jose leading us out," Dave roared with laughter. He pushed himself up from his crablike position on the ground. Bracing himself on the car, he finally confessed to the prank joke he played on us.

Until that moment, I had controlled my emotions. Words reverberating from the others were a roar in my ears. Nothing anyone said penetrated my personal bubble. I yanked off my coveralls, wadded them into a ball, headed forward at full steam, and threw them at Dave. He backed away as I lunged toward him with fists ready for battle. He was almost faster than me, but not quite. I barreled into him and shoved him to the ground. Jose stepped in between us and yanked us apart. *I could literally strangle Dave*

"So, what is the big deal? There should be no fuss. This would be such a great story to tell at school."

Behind me, Jose had balled up his fists, and I really thought he was going to deck Dave. This easily could have been a fisticuffs re-enactment of the "Fight of the Century." Dave was smart enough to put the car between them until Jose calmed down.

And only feet away found Patty droning on about the adventure.

"This was so cool, especially crawling through that tunnel. And, when the flashlight fell... Wow." Patty's adrenaline was still high, and she chattered on and on, replaying the entire night back to Mary.

Patty's back was to the guys, completely clueless as to the drama unfolding around her.

"This was such a blast, wasn't it?"

Mary stared at Patty in amazement. She had never seen such an idiot.

I let the tears roll over my cheeks, adrenaline gone.

We were all silent on the ride home, each replaying the evening in his or her mind.

From that day forward, I have always told someone where I would be.

THESE CAVES ARE IN COLORADO. MY BROTHER AND I once talked about the dumb things we did in high school and wouldn't you know it, he knew the exact location of my terrifying event.

Apparently, the caves were well known to high school explorers. Names of people and the location have been hidden or changed to protect the stupid.

THE TIE THAT BINDS

*J*had never been in such a store. I wandered up and down each aisle, rather amazed by the sheer amount of merchandise available. There were lawnmowers here, right next to the light bulbs. *There were washing machines available in the same store?* With so many items to choose from, I knew I would find what I needed in these overstuffed, narrow aisles.

"I need a new washer," I said to myself as I looked at my light-colored blouse dotted with the Rorschach-like dark stains. That would have to wait for a separate shopping trip.

From around an endcap shuffled a bespectacled gnome of a man.

"May I help you find something?" he asked.

"Yes, I am looking for those plastic things you'd use when you kidnap someone," I said.

"What?" he squeaked as if I had spoken in an alien

tongue.

"You know those white or black strips. The police use them too, when they arrest the bad guys," I replied, thinking that would help to give him a clue.

"Ma'am, come again?" he asked.

"Maybe I am not explaining this very well. The plastic strip wraps around the wrists, you thread it together, and zip it closed. Then, the hands stay tied together," I said and patiently demonstrated the process to him as I held my rough, raw, work hands in that position for him to see.

"Um… follow me," he instructed. I shuffle stepped in line behind him, several aisles over. "I believe these are what you are looking for. We refer to them as electrical ties."

I noticed his voice had a slight waver to it and his hands trembled.

"Yes, this is it exactly." I waved them in the air. "Thanks," I said to him and walked away.

I checked out and smiled at the clerk. I noticed in my peripheral vision the excited gentleman continued to point at me while trying to demonstrate bound wrists to a confused coworker. As I exited the doorway, his strange behavior puzzled me.

"You would think the man never tied up overgrown tomato plants," I murmured to myself as I strolled through the parking lot.

Spring 2017

THE WEDDING RING

I wander through the shell of a home that once vibrated with the energy of family and friends. Today it is nothing more than dust motes and old people smell.

Why it is left to me to settle matters and clear memories is beyond my imagination. Her sons left the job to me, the eldest grandchild. My only interest in the old home is her sewing box and her quilts. I will clear out the clutter, call a handyman to haul out the remaining furniture for a donation to a good cause, and consider it good.

Someone had stolen almost everything of value while she was so ill. I am sure this included her wedding ring and jewelry, as none of it could be located after her funeral. I had a suspicion I knew who might have done such a deed, but I had no proof. One day I will know for sure.

I picked my way through each room, righting what remained of the overturned chairs and end tables. The sight of wood chunks, kindling, and fire starter chips haphazardly spilling over a quilt with the Split Rail Fence pattern next to the stone fireplace horrified me.

The bedrooms had fared no better. If anything of value ever existed here, it was no longer present. There hung a framed quilted Wedding Ring block hanging askew on the wall. I straightened it as I walked by and noticed it was not lying flat in the frame. Well, that was dumb. Why straighten it as it would go home with me, anyway? One more thing to take with me. This was unusual, though, for Grandmother's work was meticulous. I could hear her saying to me, "That row isn't straight, pull it out and stitch it again." Considering the total mess surrounding me, a wrinkle in that block was minor.

I tugged on a quilt that stuck out between the mattress and box springs. I had to upend the mattress to pull it out and for an antique, it was still in good shape. *Why would she have placed it between the mattress and box springs in the first place? Was she hiding it?*

She lost at least twenty-five quilts in a home fire years ago when a fireplace ember set the roof to their old farmhouse on fire. The ones she made in the following years were as precious as gold to her. Maybe that was the answer, as logic often confused her in those later years.

I knew this particular one was a Flying Geese

pattern and one of her favorites. Back in the day, she cut the pieces for her quilts using old cardboard templates. Measuring tools weren't as exact as the equipment we have today, but her pieces were always cut true to the grain.

I took a trip to the attic and luckily enough found a few more quilts stacked in the corner, apparently not worthy of a thief's second glance. Thank goodness the prior burglars did not realize the value of a handmade quilt, especially those of antique quality. I spied the dust covered sewing box next to the pile. This was exactly what I was searching for.

The day continued as I cleaned away cobwebs and dust bunnies. I cried and laughed at all the silly memories each room held. Remembering the time I fell down the stairs brought on a good chuckle, especially since I had been warned to be extra careful. I guess I listened no more in those days than I do now.

Here was the old metal bed my uncle slept in when he was a teenager. The one with the skull and crossbones he had glued to the headboard. No way did I ever want to sleep in that bed. What an ornery old cuss. He was meaner than an anthill full of fire ants.

My bedroom upstairs was always so cold in the winter. I begged and begged for more quilts to be piled on top of me until I could no longer turn over. Visiting Grandmother was always a treat.

Feeling I could accomplish no more that day, I took the quilts I gathered and the framed block out to the car.

Remembering the quilt under the woodpile, I moaned at the thought that it might be ruined. I unstacked all the wood, rolled up the quilt, and heard a paper crackle next to the batting inside the quilt. Dark had fallen. This place was so full of mysteries, but they would have to wait for another time. The cleaning itself would take another entire day.

Once the car was unloaded, and I nestled in my favorite chair at home, I took the time to look over my treasures. First, the framed block. It certainly needed a good cleaning. Once the glass was removed, something clunked to the floor. A glistening object rolled under the coffee table. I crouched down to grab it. Gasping as my hand found a round metal object, I plopped myself right down on the floor. It was Grandmother's missing diamond wedding ring! She had hidden it in the Wedding Ring Block. I laughed so hard my sides hurt. That wise old bird. How appropriate. She was making darn sure her ring went where I would find it.

Thinking nothing could top that happy moment, I finished adoring the quilts. The last one was the crackling Split Rail Fence. I could see the stitches on the corner were unusually large, awkward, and not her style. This was another mystery as Grandmother was a master quilter. If I had done this, I would be tearing it out and doing it over again until it was perfect. I gave a small tug on the thread, pulled the edge apart, and found a note inside the block.

Well, of course, I had to read it. Who else was going to?

"I hope you found my wedding ring. You know I promised it to you. Look in the bottom of the sewing basket. It is all yours, also," she had written. On the bottom of the basket, I found her missing jewelry and another note. "Do not let anyone sell the house until you go through it carefully."

I could not have been more shocked if the moon turned purple. I certainly intended to carry out her wish. I was still laughing as I wondered what other mysteries she had planned for me.

THERE ARE NO UGLY QUILTS

*W*hile walking to the curb waiting for the traffic to pass, I looked at the bundle in my arms. To those around me, it appeared to be only a normal load of laundry. The object of my attention was a recently finished quilt.

That frosty morning, with no more thought of where I was headed other than a straight path to the dumpster, I did not see the white-bearded gentleman directly ahead of me as I plowed headlong into him.

"Where are you off to in such a hurry?" he politely inquired.

After making my apology for nearly knocking him over, I replied, "To the trash dumpster to throw away this ugly quilt."

The statement was so inconceivable to the gentleman that he was incredulous with disbelief and asked for an explanation.

With a sigh, I replied, "I made it myself, but the colors are not right, and the stitching is crooked. There are too many loose threads. My seams do not match. Obviously, this quilt is not a good one. It is ugly and the best place for it is in the trash."

After gathering his thoughts, the man's reply was sincere and to the point.

"Mother Nature does not discriminate over colors in her works of art, so why would you? Isn't the purple heather lovely next to the orange lily? Your loose threads are symbolic of the threads of life. They will unravel our lives daily until we pick up the pieces and learn to mend our ways. Consider crooked stitching to be like that of man's path. It is never straight. The adventure in life is along that path. And is there anything in this world that is perfect? Perfection is something to strive for, but it should not be our driving force."

I stared wide-eyed as the kindly old man went on. "You have your thoughts backward and confused. This quilt will warm a cold body, comfort a healing soul, and will allow a curious mind to wander with questions about you, the artist. It will become a tale for a storyteller, a puzzle for a mathematician, a field for a gardener to dream upon, and a treasure for one who has none."

"It will have a softness of touch for the blind and sweet memories for a child. It will also provide solace and a time of reflection for the quilter and happiness for the recipient."

As the tears coursed down my face, I realized there was much wisdom in the man's words. As he turned to go, he said, "To deny the giver an opportunity to present a gift robs him of happiness."

Pausing momentarily, he continued by saying, "Did you know there is an orphanage on the other side of town? Be the giver." With that, he quietly continued on his way, leaving me with only his words to remember him by.

That following Christmas season, I remembered that bearded man and his wisdom when I saw a young couple window shopping on the hustle-bustle of a winter day. They were cuddling a tiny bundle in a hand-made quilt. Watching their joy, the visit I had with the nameless man brought to mind that experience which I shall never forget. I believe words of wisdom truly do come from the most unexpected circumstances. I wondered if one day a quilt I might make would cuddle a tiny baby.

Christmas 2001 Bozeman, Montana

This is story is a composite of many events and statements people have said to me over the years that I combined into one story.

TIM AND THE PROFESSIONAL

"*Y*ou look mahvelous darlin, just mahvelous," he exaggerated his southern drawl, knowing it always left me in fits of giggles. The laugh lines etched around the corners of his eyes were proof of this man's deep sense of ongoing humor.

His comments on my manner of dress were commonplace to me. He often tucked the tags back inside my neckline or checked my fingernails for dirt after a day of gardening.

My friend, Tim hefted up a box of handout materials that I gathered for my latest project. Tim was always around when I needed extra muscle or a friendly laugh. Today, I was taking part in a lecture series for high school students on professionalism in the workplace.

The work-study program was for high school students. My topic was teaching proper interview techniques. I preferred not to use the lecture style. It was boring. My method was to use acting to keep their attention alive. The program committee asked me to do this lesson because of my business experience and as that of a community leader. My acting would be a total surprise to the students, event coordinator, and the management of the store. Teenagers were a hard crowd to work with, but I was determined to give this idea a try.

Tim chatted amiably as he drove, and we discussed the points I wanted to cover in my presentation. This demonstration was being held in a local grocery store break room. This was for convenience's sake, as many of the students worked at the store.

"I want to emphasize professional dress as in Sunday best, not some of the get-ups I see daily. Last week I had an applicant with curlers in her hair and a cup of coffee in her hand," I said. "And she set the coffee on my desk like we were visiting in my living room. I'm surprised she didn't prop her feet up as well."

As he rolled his eyes, Tim said, "Uh-huh, you tell 'em, sister."

"You would think by this time, they would know how to spell. I see fried and laid as excuses for being fired or laid-off all the time as their reasons for leaving a job."

By the time we arrived, we had left the topics of attitude, spelling, and manner of proper dressing behind and were well into our regular gossip session. Tim pulled up to the curb and sashayed around to open the limo door for me.

Oh, I forgot to mention that one of my business ventures was a limo service, and Tim often drove for me.

As we were about to enter the store, I tripped on the curb. Tim helped me up, and I continued to stumble past the enormous front of the store windows. We were still laughing at my clumsiness when the sliding doors opened at the entrance, and every cashier and guest stopped to stare at us. There were at least six busy check-out lanes of customers who came to a complete halt. *What in the world? I thought Southerners had better manners.*

"Everywhere we go, steal the show," I said, shaking my head. Tim's confident stride, six-foot-plus frame, the wave of dark hair, and those aviator glasses always drew admiring glances. He was a very handsome man.

"It is not me they are looking at, missy. You are the professional here," he said to me as we made our way to the store's break room. He opened the door for me and set my supplies on the side table.

"People, people," the startled manager called the ear-splitting noise in the room to order after our abrupt entrance.

Tim grinned, gave me a wave, and left the room.

Mighty fast exit. He didn't even wait for me to intro- duce him. You would think the handsome peacock couldn't wait to get out the door. That is not like him at all.

Tim was barely outside the classroom door before he bent over double with a deep belly laugh.

"Now, how is she going to pull that professional bit off in those cut-off shorts over polka dot tights, a dirty T-shirt, and ankle-breaking heels?" he asked himself. "That hair is teased so stiff a bird could make a nest there. They are gonna kick her out of here. She has really lost it this time. Wait till she tries to explain fried or laid. There is never a dull moment with that woman around."

THIS IS A TRUE STORY. TO SAY THE STUDENTS, THE educational event coordinator, and the store manager were shocked is an understatement. I acted out the scenes which I encountered daily in my office as a temporary employment manager and entertained the students to a point that in later times, they would stop me on the street and tell me they were in one of those student groups. They asked me to perform this twice more for the school system, and yes, I was in my "professional" costume. The looks I received walking through the high school were hilarious, much like the ones I received at the grocery store. There is a teaching video of giving me this "lecture" floating around some-

179

where. I have never seen it. Tim and I have shared many funny times during our friendship years, but this by far was the most outlandish one.

Newnan, Georgia 1993

TOMMY THE LEPRECHAUN

AKA THE DAY I MET A LEPRECHAUN

"*H*ow may I help you today?" I inquired as the door chimed, indicating a customer had entered the floral shop. *What did one do when approached by a leprechaun on the warmest afternoon in July?*

The day I met this stranger, I only stared, stammered, and tripped over my feet on my way to the guest desk to offer whatever assistance a leprechaun required. I had never seen a real leprechaun, but here stood a vision of one right before my eyes.

I guessed he measured five-foot-three inches tall, dressed in the typical elfin style with a pointed hat, an emerald-green velvet suit, a walking staff, and boots that curled up over his toes. His weathered face resembled the creased lines of a crumpled brown paper sack, but the hypnotic, sea-green eyes were those of a much younger, mischievous man.

If he noticed my gawking at him, his demeanor did not reflect any acknowledgment of my rude manners. He asked me "Would you by chance have the right size balloons for twisting into animal shapes?"

"Why, yes, I certainly do." I sighed to myself. This made perfect sense. He was a street performer. Our family-friendly town held events in the community park and country markets both on Wednesdays and Saturdays where vendors sold their wares, and all manner of performers were invited to attend. The items he toted: a guitar case, a backpack, and a walking stick, cemented the fact in my mind that he would hang out in our area for one of the town's hot summer celebrations.

We made the transaction, and I passed along a bit of information about our local events. As the shop had filled, the man took his cue to leave. Out the door, he bounced before I could ask his name or wring the details out of him about his unusual garb or planned gig.

"Thank you for stopping…" were the words I blurted before *his* words filtered back to me as the door chimed once again.

"Have a fantasmagorical day!"

"Huh?" *I guessed that was what a leprechaun said.*

During the following week, after working hours, I strolled along Main Street and stopped to buy my favorite lemonade from a sidewalk vendor. As I sipped the sweet treat, I heard the strumming of a guitar, off-key singing, and giggling children.

I had tried to peer down the sidewalk to glimpse the

musician, but unfortunately, two impish girls had blocked my view. Since Curiosity is my middle name, I marched forward on a mission to check out the excitement.

I caught my lemonade mid-air as I skidded to a halt when I recognized "the leprechaun." From jaunty hat to pointy toes, here was the elf having a gay old time. *What in the world was he doing sitting in the middle of the sidewalk strumming his guitar and singing? This was not event central… or maybe it was.*

His singing stopped only moments before my arrival. He had started a storytelling ditty for the children as his fingers played over the worn strings. In between the nonsense jingles and rhymes that he had written, he would place his guitar in his lap and twist a balloon animal within direct eye contact of a dazzled child. His gestures and facial features showed kindness and benevolent love, which made me even more curious as to his motivation to be a busker.

He sat next to his open guitar case, which is the universal clue to drop in a donation for a street performer's work. From the amount of money, I spied in the case, it appeared a brisk business would net him a fat wallet that evening. Once the youngsters moved on, I sat down on the sidewalk next to him and began a conversation.

"Will you tell me the story about your life and work?" I asked.

The kindness of his words flowed as he said, "I do

this because laughter brings me great joy. I returned from the war years ago. I saw too much pain, and I told myself 'no more.' My intention is to 'do no harm' and spend the rest of my life doing what gives me and others around me happiness."

We passed the time chatting about his lifestyle. He roamed the highways from city to city, making his livelihood in this manner. Many times, the thoughtfulness of others had found him in a warm bed at night rather than sleeping under a bridge, his clothing cleaned, and solid, hearty meals provided for him at no cost. It was apparent he was well-liked in the areas he visited and continued to be welcomed by all.

He had said, when people asked him, "How can you prove you're a leprechaun?"

He would reply, "How can you prove I'm not?"

As I readied myself to leave, he handed me his calling card. It was his custom to leave his 'guests' with a pale green card that stated the name 'Tommy the Leprechaun' and granted the holder of the card one free wish. Tommy stayed for the weeklong festival and could be heard all up and down the streets singing and playing his instrument. He never forgot to offer the words "Have a fantasmagorical day!"

It was years later when I saw his obituary in the newspaper. They listed his story, picture, and name as Tommy the Leprechaun, and included was his leprechaun image on the front page. I called the nursing home where he had lived out his last days to seek condolence information. He had left his proper name and one person to call upon his passing for the medical staff only. It was his wish that no one was to know the details of his life or his actual name other than 'Tommy the Leprechaun.'

This event took place in Bozeman, Montana in 1996. Tommy passed away in Missoula, Montana, in 2003. It was his custom to travel between the larger cities from Billings, Boze-man, Butte, and Missoula to entertain those who would listen. I still have my 'wish' card.

TURTLE IS A DOG

"You are a turtle, NOT a dog," said Hank for the hundredth time. "I am your best friend. Why won't you listen to me?"

"I do not want to be a turtle," said Turtle. "I want to be a dog."

At the moment, they were both basking in the sunlight. The duo had taken the short walk to the sprawling oak tree next to their human's house. Turtle couldn't walk as fast as Hank, as he was a gigantic dog, so they compromised and let Turtle rest his legs while they sunbathed close to home.

"Since you are my best friend, I think it is my duty to explain to you exactly why I can be a dog, Mr. Smarty," said the slowpoke pal.

"Oh, here we go," huffed Hank. "Go ahead, enlighten me."

First off, my friend Zoe is a dog.

"So, what! So are Dusty, Mandy, and Cassie. Big deal. They don't want to be turtles."

"How do you know; did you ever ask them? She says there are no rules, I can do whatever I want, and you are not the boss of me."

"Turtle, you don't look like a dog! You don't even have a dog name! Turtle is your name."

"What do looks have to do with it? Everyone looks different. I have four feet like a dog, I take walks like a dog, I swim in water like a dog, I eat like a dog, and I have people friends like a dog does. As far as a name goes, I didn't pick the name. What about Hank for a name? That happens to be a people name."

"Wait a minute, you do not eat like a dog, eat in the water, dogs eat out of a bowl or chew a bone on the ground," grumped Hank.

"I still eat, don't I, where and how doesn't matter."

Hank was on the verge of growling out a response when their owner, Jacob, stepped around the corner. Jacob loved his pets, and he understood he was their 'human' and was there to obey their every wish. Today was no exception. Sensing a problem was brewing, he flopped down and began to referee.

"Hi, my pals. How has your day been going?" he asked.

Before his friends could cordially reply, Hank barked as he pointed his paw at his idle pal. "He wants to be a dog, and he won't understand why he can't be one."

"Jacob, Hank won't listen to reason!" piped up the disgusted turtle.

"Well, how do you two plan to solve this minor disagreement?"

"Minor!" They both exploded, and then babbled at once about who was right and who was wrong. Jacob watched and listened until they wore themselves out. Then he picked up Hank's leash and told him it was time for his walk and obedience lesson. He told Turtle they would be back shortly to put him back in his tank, and he could continue to sunbathe until they returned.

In cases of this nature, Jacob had found it best to separate the two until they could return to their loving natural state of mind. Golden retrievers were always docile and turtles so placid, one barely knew they were around. That was in a normal scenario. Turtle was different. In his case, the minute he was out of his tank, he would roam the house. He would walk everywhere, over the rugs, under the couch, through the toys on the floor, and right across your legs if you were sitting on the floor. He would cuddle next to anyone who was willing to pick him up and set him on his favorite blanket on the sofa. Mom wasn't so crazy about that idea. *It is no wonder he wants to be a dog. He acts like one. How to help these two solve this problem?*

Jacob had taken this 'turtle-dog' problem upon himself to find a solution for the two squabblers. He asked Hank to call in the neighborhood gang of dogs for a meeting. When they gathered, it was more like a convention. Jacob certainly didn't expect such a turnout. Once he had the group's attention, he explained the problem and asked if anyone had a solution to Turtle's dilemma. Aloof Afghan hounds didn't want Turtle to be admitted into the dog's world. Irish wolfhounds were a friendly bunch, and they didn't mind if it made Turtle happy. Beagles, bloodhounds, and basset hounds wanted to sniff out more details before they gave an opinion. If he didn't waddle in the middle of a hunt, the sporting dogs had no problem with adding Turtle to their gang. Poodles continued to file their nails and paid no attention whatsoever. So, the meeting went on in this vein until the pack was exhausted and ready to head home to their bowl of dog chow and a comfy bed.

"Asking your dog buddies wasn't much help, was it, Hank?"

"We will figure it out, Jacob, we always do."

As time passed, it was obvious a sadness had overcome Turtle, and no amount of coaxing could bring him out of his shell. That is until Jacob stumbled across the answer on their street corner. He gathered up his human friends with their dogs, who Hank and Turtle knew well, and they all attacked the plan with eagerness and good humor.

That Sunday, Jacob approached Turtle with a leash Jacob had made specially to fit Turtle. "We are going for a walk, Turtle. No arguments, observe all that is happening, and you MUST do everything I tell you to do, understand? We are proving today that you can be a dog."

"Really, you are not teasing me?"

"This is too important; I would not tease you about this."

His friend Zoe was there also with her human and she said, "Remember, always be who you want to be and only do what you want to do."

Turtle watched and listened carefully to all his friends and their humans as they proceeded to line up. Penny and her human Jenn were in front of Turtle and Jacob, and slowly each pair moved forward to visit with a lady holding a clipboard. Eventually, it was Turtle and Jacob's turn to approach the lady.

Miss Clipboard was not looking at the duo when she told them to step forward. She had been talking to another lady at a table close by, then turned and gasped in surprise as she looked at the pair waiting for her.

"Young man, this is an obedience trial," Miss Clipboard said as she gave them a questioning look.

"Yes, ma'am, I know it is," replied Jacob.

"For dogs," she pointed out.

"Ma'am, the signs and literature all say obedience trial, nothing says it is for dogs only, so we are here to participate."

Miss Clipboard appeared stunned and conferred with the other members of the event. Jacob was correct, and she had no choice but to let Turtle try. The scowl on her face portrayed her thoughts. But she would go along with the rules.

As Jacob had already told Turtle to pay attention to all directions, they were both ready.

"Forward," Miss Clipboard commanded, and Turtle and Jacob walked forward.

"Halt. About face." Boy and turtle obeyed. The amazed judge knew the next command would mess them up. "Fast forward!" There may have been a small amount of increased speed, but that was debatable in her mind. "Halt. You may now join the others."

"Good job, Turtle," Jacob praised him and patted his shell.

"Jacob, you didn't tell me this was what I had to do to be a dog. Am I a dog now?"

"No, we are not finished yet."

Shortly, Miss Clipboard called all owners and their dogs back to the ring. She instructed all the humans to tell their dogs to 'sit and stay' and then cross the ring away from them. Turtle sat on his hind legs like the other dogs had done and pushed his shell up to a slant with his front legs. They all sat without moving until their owners returned.

Then, the order came to 'down and stay' and once again the owners crossed the ring to watch their pets lie still until they returned. Turtle was an expert at this task. After this part of the trial, all the participants left the ring and waited for their scores. A score in the lower 70s would mean 'no pass' but there wasn't a problem with

Turtle's score. His only lower mark was his fast walk. He passed his obedience test, though with a great score of 96! The doggie group and humans cheered for him.

"Now, do you feel like a dog?" Hank asked. "Obedience is important, and trials are a way of proving that fact in a dog's world. And you did very well. We even have a new name for you."

"That's it? That's all it takes to be a dog?"

"Well, you said you already did everything a dog does, so this is the last thing to prove it, plus adding your new name."

"Okay, it all feels strange, so what is my new name?" asked Turtle.

"Dee-oh-gee, get it? D-O-G, Deeohgee," said Hank gleefully.

"Oh, okay, sure, I get it, thanks," said Turtle.

"Woof, woof, hurray, to you, too, Turtle," said Hank sarcastically. "We thought you would be way more excited than this."

"I guess, I am tired from all of that walk, run, halt stuff. I really am grateful to all of you for arranging this day for me." He saw Zoe standing on the sidelines with her doggie smile and a wink.

Jacob suggested the dogs go on home alone and he would hang with his friends. The dogs all knew the shortcut home, and they needed the time together to visit. Brezzie, the Bichon asked if they might take the path near the creek through the park. It was a sunny day, perfect for a dip in the cool pool where the creek flowed over the rocks. Zoe, the small Yorkshire terrier, preferred to stay on the side of the pool watching the others play.

Brezzie said, "Zoe, please take a dip in the pool with me."

"Thank you for asking, but I really enjoy watching you all enjoy the water." They were here to play, and he obliged her by doing a cannonball jump off the rock into the deeper end of the pond. Zoe sputtered as the droplets rained down on her shiny black and tan coat. With the rain from the day before and these consistent belly flops and cannonball splashes, the mud puddle around her continued to grow.

Even Turtle was having a good bit of fun as he pulled his legs into his shell, gave a cowboy whoop, and slid down the mud into the cool water. He was so happy swimming in this big people pond. It had much more room than his tank at home.

As they all dog paddled and dove for sticks, one by one they realized Zoe was not yapping her head off as usual.

"Everyone stop making noise!" Hank snarled out a warning.

A tiny 'yip, yip' came from a few feet out into the pond. Apparently, Zoe had slipped down the muddy bank and fell into the water. Her black eyes opened wide in terror, and her mouth gasped for air each time she bobbed up. Then, as if pulled by an invisible force, she would disappear below the surface again.

One by one her friends swam to the spot where she had last surfaced, each hoping he or she would be the one to find her and save her from drowning. They all reached the bubbles and rings of water where they saw her last, but no Zoe. When fear overtook the group, her head and body slowly lifted out of the water, and her body floated to the shoreline. *What bit of magic was this?*

Turtle earlier had taken time out to bask on the bank and saw what had happened. A natural swimmer, he immediately dove beneath the waterline. That is when he saw Zoe's legs trying to kick. But she was not making progress as she slid farther down into the pool. He then dove below her, swam up underneath her body, and settled her on his turtle shell. Up they rose until she reached fresh air. Turtle was used to swimming and being underwater, but Zoe was not. He swam on until he could dig his claws into the slope of the bank. The big dogs rushed to help her climb off of Turtle's shell, where they rolled her about and pushed on her until she spewed up the creek water.

"Turtle, you saved Zoe. You really are a wonderful dog. Saving her took such bravery."

"No, Hank, I am a turtle, and turtles swim like this every day. It is not bravery. It is normal. Not one of you knew Zoe was terrified of the water and couldn't swim, did you?" asked Turtle as he looked at them. "It was her greatest fear, and no one cared to find out about her except me."

After Zoe assured each dog that she was okay, they lifted her up onto Hank's back so he could give her a ride home. Exhaustion overtook her, and she could barely move on her own. They all felt ashamed that they tried to coax her into being a swimming dog.

That evening, Turtle had a talk with Hank and Jacob. "I have thought this over. I have decided I would rather be a turtle than a dog. Being a dog isn't such a big deal, and I really didn't need to prove to anyone that I could do all those things. I can do them, hang out with the dogs and still be me. So, thank you for all you have done for me, but I shall remain Turtle. I only had to realize it myself."

Zoe always said, "Be who you want to be, and always do what you want to do."

2020–Moline, Illinois

Our family has a turtle whose name really is Turtle, and in his turtle heart or brain, he believes he is a dog. He really does all the things mentioned in this story. Hank is real and so is Zoe. Poor Hank let him crawl around on him until he has enough turtle playtime and then he finally moves. All the dogs named in this story have been our family dogs. Zoe is always curious and pokes her nose at Turtle. And Zoe does NOT like water.

WALLFLOWER DAYS REMEMBERED

When I was in the seventh grade, we had a new student, not a charmer by any means, nor was he knock out gorgeous, but money, culture, and a father who earned a high Air Force officer's rank gave him status. So, he gave a semi-formal dance at the Officer's Club in Colorado Springs, and he invited the entire class to attend. Students with whom I attended junior high school in those years participated in cotillion dance lessons regularly, and semi-formal meant nothing more than a bit fancier than Sunday best. But, to those of us who were not in that social set, and especially the mother of this girl, it meant a whole different style.

Days before this big deal dance, I came home from school to find a box on my bed. Mind you, I hadn't even decided if I really wanted to go to this cliquish dance or not. From that moment on, the gift on my bed committed me to the event. Inside the big white rectangular department store box rested a red dress. I should not say rested, for as soon as I lifted the lid from the box, a poof of red chiffon took on a life of its own and erupted out of the constraints of the box.

To my surprise and horror, I saw yards and yards of red chiffon pop out at me ala the 1950 style fluff. Oh, my. *What was I supposed to do now?* Mom was so proud of buying it for me. Well, at least she picked out the right color. Red had always been my favorite. We were an extremely poor family, and I do not know where she found the money to buy what she considered a semi-formal dress. So off I went, and you guessed it, I was the wilting wallflower of all wallflowers.

No one danced with me, let alone approach me except the honored birthday boy himself, which was of course his obligation. I kept that dress for years. Later into our adult years, my younger sister told me how sorry she felt for me having to wear that dress, so you can imagine how I must have looked if my sister imagined a red fluff ball going to the ball.

Those must have been my gawky years, for I went to a band dance within the same time frame in a two-piece white suit, and once again this happened to me. My only dance partner was the band director and the class playboy (you can bet he didn't do this on his own). I went home crying my eyes out. To this day, I don't wear white suits, but red remains my favorite color.

There were definitely no more dances and social outings of that nature for me during the junior high years. By high school, I had grown past all the wallflower days. Eventually, as girls gossip, and cliques happen, I learned the reason for these "fails" at dances. I wonder, in this devious mind of mine, how those young ladies raised their children. The rites of passage may be painful, but they are character-building.

Colorado Springs, Colorado 1963 event age thirteen

YOU CAN HAVE HER!

*C*hug, chug, chug rattled the dreaded sound of a dying engine.

"Mom, what is wrong with the car?" Andy asked. "We're gonna be late." It would mortify him if he entered the classroom after the session began. He despised being the center of attention.

"I know that son," I said as she pulled to the side of the road as the engine died. I hopped out, yanked up the hood, placed the hold-up bar in the slot, and peered over the fender as if I knew a fan belt from a fuel line. Cars honked as they whizzed by.

With a sidelong glance, I saw my son slithering inch by inch to the floorboards of the van. The red and blue lights flashed as the police car breezed through the green light signal and pulled over behind our immobile vehicle.

No wonder he is having a meltdown. Makes sense. Oh, this ought to be good.

"What seems to be the problem, ma'am?" the confused officer asked.

"My car just plain stopped."

"Let me have a look – Oh. . . I see the problem. The battery cable has jiggled loose." He tightened the cable and asked me to try the ignition. I turned on the key, gave it the gas, and the engine kicked right over.

After assuring me that all was fine with the car, he performed the required protocol, and requested my papers and license. He looked at the registration and the picture on the license, then again repeated the process of inspecting my license.

There was something amiss here, and he needed to find the answer. He informed me he must call in the information for regulation purposes.

"Mom! We are going to be late, really late."

"Son, I can't make him move any faster."

When the officer returned to the car, he respectfully told me, "Ma'am, this picture doesn't look like you at all. I may have to take you in for impersonating someone other than yourself."

"You can have her," came Andy's voice from the floorboards on the passenger side of the van.

"I understand, son. I surely do," said the officer. He turned away to keep his grin from showing to the hunkered down boy.

"Ma'am, I hesitate to ask you this, but why in the

world in the middle of August heat would you be dressed up like a Christmas elf?"

I replied, "I model in costume every summer for the children's gifted program at the college."

Wanting the officer to realize how bad things really were, Andy bellowed, "Well, sir, if you think this is bad, you should have seen her in the devil suit standing by the shooting flames when we lit up the pottery fire pit."

The officer broke out in a hearty laugh as he shook his head. "Oh, you poor kid. Ma'am, you are free to go."

This is a true story, every word. I was an artist's model in a program called College for Kids at Blackhawk College, East Moline, Illinois. Each summer for two weeks I wore a different costume each day to the art studio where the students drew my likeness.

August 1985

ZOE AND CLOUD HAVE A MYSTERY

*Z*oe, a five-pound black and tan Yorkshire terrier and the blinding white, smaller mini four-pound Maltese named Cloud, were inseparable. They discussed the daily news during their morning meeting at a hole in the weathered wooden fence separating their two yards. Their owners, Bessie, and Georgia, two feisty older ladies knew the two were safe if they were in each other's company.

Playing "tent" was their favorite past-time. An old stiff canvas shopping bag with a hard-plastic insert opened like a tent when laid on its side. The two crawled into their fortress for girl talk or naptime.

On this day, the weather forecast showed a strong windstorm. Since the tent was mobile, the two each latched onto one of the web straps to move it to a safer area. When they were within sight of their goal, a slight breeze turned into a heavy updraft.

The gust blew into the bag, lifting not only the bag, but both dogs off their feet. Fearful of falling from the sky if either dog released her bite on the strap, both clamped her jaw down harder. As they dangled in the wind, the balloon bag landed in the neighbor man's yard amidst flying papers, plastic grocery store bags, and dead leaves.

A man with gray hair whipping about his head skidded around the corner of the house, nearly losing his balance. He was throwing his arms around in windmill fashion. He began chasing Zoe and Cloud back and forth through the yard. Frightened more of the raging person than the storm, they dropped their hold on the bag, dodged his flying feet, and headed for the sidewalk. The howling man pitched the canvas bag after them.

Out of breath and seriously frightened out of their wits, they escaped back home to rest on the porch. Neither understood what had happened in the last few minutes.

The girls instantly named this strange man Mr. Grumpo or Mr. G for short.

Cloud's home was on the left side of Zoe's house. Mr. Grumpo lived to the right of Zoe's residence. Between Cloud and Zoe's yards was the grayed, splintery, wobbly, and broken wooden fence. Mr. Grumpo had a chain-link fence down the left side of his front yard dividing his and Zoe's yards. The mini-Yorkie had a bird's-eye view of his yard from her upstairs window. She could see or hear him every morning complaining about one thing or another. Today it was his missing newspaper.

For whatever reason, this evolved into a routine. He would call the newspaper office each morning, offering his opinion of both the carrier and the newspaper. The conversation irritated him even more since the customer service lady refused to argue with him. The fence between the two homes hindered Zoe's vision. She figured she was high enough on the second floor that she could watch his home and find the cause of the missing newspaper. If she solved this mystery, she could put an end to the noisy ravings of this crazy man.

The next morning both girls pushed through their doggy doors long before their human owners were awake. Cloud wiggled through the hole in the wooden fence, and both fur balls trotted to a corner of the back-yard behind the doghouse.

Zoe's owner had a flair for the creative. That back-yard doghouse looked more like a castle than a dog's house. It even had a tower and a drawbridge over a mini moat. It certainly was a home for a princess, but this girl was living in a people house NOT a doghouse. Cloud wanted to stay in the castle while Zoe did the exploring. She didn't mind being a princess or even a queen. She was a prima donna, so living in a castle would be normal for her.

In the past, Zoe had dug a tunnel under her own fence, so they were free to roam about the street visiting other dog friends in the hood. This, of course, was an unknown fact to their human owners or the fur would fly. Most likely the dust would fly, as the dogs really needed their fur to stay on their bodies. For certain, a time out would have been issued if they were caught outside of the fence. Every time it was time to go visiting or exploring, Zoe had to coax Miss Prissy out of the castle and through the escape hatch.

Zoe ran into the front yard of Mr. G's at the exact moment the paper plopped onto the front porch. She bit down on one side of the rolled paper and dragged it to an azalea bush at the end of the flower garden. Cloud peeped out from her safe spot on the side of Mr. G's house.

Soft dirt surrounded the bushes, and anyone stopping to retrieve the paper would leave a footprint. She could then follow these footprints after the culprit snuck away. Detective Zoe was on the hunt.

All morning the pups waited and watched from Zoe's yard. Only joggers and dog walkers appeared. Yet to their amazement, the newspaper disappeared once again. The two nosy pups peered closely through the chain-link fence and could see no footprints. Mr. G was so angry. He hopped up and down, making spitting noises with his mouth. The girls rolled over in laughter.

There had to be a solution to this unusual situation. Zoe had also noticed a disturbance in spots in Mr. G's flower garden. He was so furious. He loved dirtying his hands, but he always smoothed the soil flat after he finished playing in the dirt. Zoe thought this was great, as she loved to dig and make the dirt fly. *Why smooth it out? What was the fun in that?*

"I don't understand why you like to play in the dirt," Cloud would always say. "I would be in so much trouble if I let my paws and legs get that dirty. My human would put me in the bath with water and bubbly stuff all over me. Then, I would sneeze and shiver. No way would I ever want to be like you, Zoe, and make such a mess. No way!"

"Come on Cloud, it won't be that bad." Zoe had insisted. Cloud could not talk Zoe out of her sleuthing quest. The mischievous Yorkie tried hard but could not convince Cloud of her latest idea to find the scoundrel who was creating such chaos with Mr. G.

"Every time anything went wrong at his house, he stomped over to my house and told my human how much he disliked dogs as if it was our fault these things happened," Zoe had growled to Cloud many times. There was a mystery here, and she was determined to solve it.

Miss Bessy's habit was to turn on the sprinkler every evening to water the grass. Zoe pulled the sprinkler closer to the fence line, and let the water make mud on the edge of Mr. G's flower bed. This way she could see any footprints left behind, for sure. Miss Bessy's yard would still be watered, and no one would be the wiser.

If Cloud were not such a Fraidy Cat, this chore would have been so much easier. "She could just be that way," Zoe thought.

She tugged the hose over to the fence all by herself. This problem would all be solved by morning.

Life wasn't looking so good the next morning. What Zoe had not counted on was that the sprinkler would flood Mr. G's sprouting flower garden. Not only were there no obvious footprints as evidence, but dirt and flowers floated everywhere in gigantic puddles.

Mr. G was stomping mad AGAIN. Zoe tried not to look guilty. Cloud couldn't help herself and flopped over, laughing.

Zoe quietly slunk into the house before anyone could realize what she had done. She gave herself a self-imposed time out. The garden was replanted, but the dug-up holes continued to reappear.

Zoe pondered this problem for several days. Cloud was still not willing to partake in the next nocturnal, adventurous outing.

She waited until the deepest dark of the night and padded ever so lightly to the garden. She dug furiously into the disturbed soil until she hit something soft with a terrible odor. More dirt flew, uncovering the stinky object. Bewildered, she sat there, staring.

"Oh, no…. yuk," she moaned and tried to cover her nose.

As fast as she had uncovered the smelly thing, she quickly piled the dirt back where it was. No treasure here. She scampered back home, shaking her head at this latest development.

"I can't tell Cloud about this yet. She will only roll

her eyes and stick that little nose of hers in the air. I can hear her say, I told you so," Zoe said out loud.

Summer scooted forward. Flowers bloomed, and the dogs played together daily. Without warning, one unusually mild summer afternoon, Mr. G began his clown-like windmill moves, yelping at the top of his lungs. Both dogs and their humans sat still on Bessie's porch and watched the circus act. Minutes later, when he calmed himself, he told them why he was so upset.

"My slippers went missing. I left them on the front porch to dry and now they are gone."

"Missing slippers? How could slippers be missing?" everyone asked. They all searched the yard, under bushes, even in the trash bin. Still no slippers. They were on the porch drying because he washed them. Where the slippers were drying before now sat a teddy bear. He was a well-worn teddy bear with part of his fur missing and one ear barely hanging on.

"Mr. G certainly could not wear a teddy bear on his feet," thought Zoe.

Cloud now agreed with Zoe that there was a mystery at Mr. G's house.

On their afternoon walk. Zoe realized someone now lived in the old Mayfield house. It had been an empty house since Mr. Mayfield moved away. Now, a rich green grass and white topped clover grew in the yard and jewel like flowers bordered the sidewalk.

"Did you know it was rumored the house was haunted?" Zoe said. That was way cool to Zoe. It made Cloud tremble to think of ghosts.

Zoe whispered to her sidekick, "There must be a dog living there. I saw a water bowl and a chewed-up toy on the porch." Another idea floated into Zoe's pesky, playful mind.

"I am not about to go anywhere near a haunted house," Cloud growled through her gritted teeth.

"*Cloud was such a baby*," Zoe thought to herself. She knew she would have to venture out by herself.

That afternoon while the old ladies napped, the adventurous Zoe squeezed out under the fence and trotted down the street. She scratched at the front door of the Mayfield house.

"No ghost lived here with such a beautiful yard and a dog bowl on the porch," Zoe continued telling herself. The door complained with a rusty groan. Zoe jumped.

Yikes, the ghost is approaching.

She ran behind a wooden bench. A man in a wheel-chair peered out. A handsome Golden Retriever wiggled out behind him and tossed his head from side to side.

"What do you see, old boy?" The man asked what Dusty saw as the dog poked about the bench until he chased Zoe out. By then, the gentleman had wheeled himself out of the door and onto the wooden stoop.

Zoe gasped at Dusty when she saw the man had Mr. G's slippers on his feet. Of course, the man did not understand her, but Dusty did. Dusty gave a sheepish smile as the gentleman looked puzzled. Mr. Wheelchair Man gestured for Dusty to invite his friend in for a visit.

All three went inside the house. The man gave Zoe and Dusty each a jerky snack. They chased a ball around the room. Zoe scooted it with her nose while Dusty retrieved it, making it all slobbery. She liked the braided tug toy better since she could bite it and play tug with Dusty or the Wheelchair Man.

Dusty and Zoe soon went outside to explore the yard. Dusty confided his owner's story to Zoe. Now she put the complete mystery together. The trick would be how to make the humans understand what she was about to do next.

The next day Zoe convinced Cloud to help her.

"Come on, Cloud, you gotta help me. I even promise never to ask for your help. . . ever again," Zoe begged.

Cloud woofed back at her. "As if I would believe that. You will always ask. I know for sure that Georgia, my human, would never follow me. She might listen to the racket and scold me, but she would never follow me. Are you nuts?"

Zoe would not take 'no' for an answer.

She commanded Cloud, "Make sure you do your job perfectly, Little Missy. This is beyond important." Zoe always heard her human call her that, so she guessed they were words you said when you really were serious.

The next morning, they both scooted out under the fence, causing the worst racket on Mr. G's front porch. They continued barking and running around, creating noise. Bessie and Georgia came running. Mr. G paid attention to them because he didn't like dogs, and he especially would not put up with this noise. The dogs would not be calm, nor would they be caught. It was like a calf roping rodeo in the front yard.

The timing had to be precise if both dogs were to take off down the street. Zoe saw Mr. G's brand-new baseball cap and snagged it right off of his footstool. It still had the price tag on it. She flew down the dirty sidewalk as fast as her stubby legs would carry her, dragging that hat beside her. Meanwhile, Cloud weaved in and out of the screaming adults' legs so they could not catch Zoe. No one tripped, which was hard to believe.

Finally arriving at Dusty's house, the doggie train stopped cold. The old gent was on his porch reading Mr. G's newspaper. He had no socks on but was again wearing the missing slippers.

Mr. G was at the caboose end on the doggy train. Stumped for words which was strange for a man who never was at a loss for words, he only stared. Zoe dropped the hat on the porch and both dogs flopped down in the overgrown yard. Dusty retrieved the hat and wagged his tail while returning it to Mr. G. He even gave Mr. G his best doggy smile.

Bessy and Georgia gasped at this most unusual sight. They also believed the house had been empty and haunted.

"Hello, we are Bessy and Georgia. We are the

owners of those very naughty dogs, Zoe and Cloud," they finally puffed out. Obviously, the old ladies did not have the energy their dogs thought they did. The dogs were still full of energy and plainly delighted at being the masterminds of this little outing.

The new neighbor introduced himself. His name was Charley, and his dog was Dusty. Charley continued by saying, "Every day Dusty here keeps bringing newspapers home, for which I am at a loss to understand. Then Dusty's old teddy bear has disappeared, and a pair of slippers arrived."

The ladies realized then that he was a lonely person, but more importantly, he could not afford the things they all took for granted. Dusty Dog was taking care of his best friend.

Zoe whispered to Cloud, "I also knew the smelly buried treasure in Mr. G's flower bed was fish. It seemed Mr. Charley had put part of his dinner fish in Dusty's dog bowl, as he didn't have any dog food for him. Since Dusty didn't like fish, he had a found a place to hide it."

"And Miss Cloud, I figured out why we couldn't see footprints in the dirt by the azalea bushes where I hid the newspaper. The dirt was too hard and Dusty didn't weigh enough to make a paw print. He had scooted by with all the other dogs and their owners. Mystery solved, thank you very much," Zoe gleefully said, and strutted about. "Next time pay attention when I need your help."

Mr. G said, "Charley, if you will keep Dusty home until after I have read the paper, I will bring it down to you every day."

What? Mr. Grumpo being nice? That is a switch!

The ladies thought a daily afternoon tea break with the two gents would give them a reason to check on the lonely neighbor. They could bake him some goodies and casseroles to make sure he was eating properly.

Now the dogs had a new playmate, Mr. Grumpo had a gardening pal, and the ladies had someone to fuss over. The best of all was now Mr. G realized dogs are not bad.

Normal, Illinois–2015

Zoe, Cloud, and Dusty are actual dogs. Bessie and Georgia are real people, only their names have been changed. All three dogs act exactly as the story portrays them. The story was written for a friend's grandchild.

ACKNOWLEDGMENTS

A heartfelt thank you to goes to Andy Dena, Diane Mulberger Olsen, Gail Roberson Williams, Vicki Plumb Boldt, Nancy Dyer Ramacitti, Judy Wilcox, Jane Quinn, MaryAnne Harbour, ConnieLee Hilborn, Pastor Phoebe Coryea, Anne Fifield, Dana Brown, Jerri Schlenker, and Mark Nolan. Over the years, the friends and authors in this list suggested I collect my stories and write a book. I figured if they had enough belief in me, maybe I should also.

Thank you to my Beta readers, Anne Fifield, Lisa Cherry, and Kiersten Marquet who kept the comments coming and the characters from wandering off. Last but not least, to Andy Dena, my son, who is not afraid to tell me something stinks, and always keeps me on my toes when it comes to writing. Even though I don't say it often enough, to him, I am most grateful.

My love of reading and writing has resulted in this

collection. I will always be indebted to Diane Olsen Mulberger, who, since our high school years has kept me giggling, willingly shared her butterscotch Rice Krispies Treats with me, and will always be a wonderful source of inspiration.

Most importantly, I am so appreciative and thankful to Jerri Schlenker who had the magic words to lead me on this journey. I thank her for the work in cover art, formatting, and counseling on writing. It was meant to be this way, as no one other than Jerri had ever been able to convince me to walk this path.

I chuckle as I think of my children, Andrew Jr., and Jennifer, who many times had to be coaxed into reading my words. Later work may include their antics, but I have spared them embarrassment this time. . . well maybe.

And as always, my love goes to my faithful dogs, who kept my feet warm as I typed away. All were well-loved but most especially, Bernie and Zoe.

Barbara, an Illinois native writes from her cozy nook as she gazes over a pond full of geese and ducks. On many days it is more gazing than writing.

Her writing develops from memories of family experiences, various compilations of events in her life, and her love of animals. Barbara spends her free time oil painting, quilting, knitting, and playing with her Yorkie, Zoe.

Made in the USA
Middletown, DE
05 September 2021